THE
MOTORWAY
QUIZ BOOK

1000 QUESTIONS TO MAKE
MOTORWAY TRAVEL FUN

Christopher Pick

JAVELIN BOOKS
POOLE · NEW YORK · SYDNEY

First published in the UK 1987 by Javelin Books,
Link House, West Street, Poole, Dorset, BH15 1LL

Copyright © 1987 Christopher Pick

Distributed in the United States by
Sterling Publishing Co., Inc.,
2 Park Avenue, New York, NY 10016

Distributed in Australia by
Capricorn Link (Australia) Pty Ltd,
PO Box 665, Lane Cove, NSW 2066

British Library Cataloguing in Publication Data

Pick, Christopher
    The motorway quiz book : 1000 questions to
    make motorway travel fun.
    1. Express highways — Great Britain —
    History — Miscellanea 2. Great Britain —
    Miscellanea
    I. Title
    941'.0076   DA632

ISBN 0 7137 1866 8

Typeset in Monophoto Plantin by August Filmsetting, St Helens
Printed and bound in Great Britain by
Anchor Brendon Ltd
Tiptree, Essex

CONTENTS

QUESTIONS

A1(M)

A1(M) HERTFORDSHIRE

Junction 23 (M25) to Junction A
1 On its way north from London, the A1 passes through Finchley, where Mrs Thatcher is the MP. What is the ceremony called at which a Prime Minister accepts his or her seals of office from the Queen?
2 How many Labour Prime Ministers have there been?

Junctions A to B
3 Bill Sykes, one of Dickens' best-known characters, is said to have visited the Eight Bells Inn in Hatfield. In which novel does Bill Sykes appear?

Junctions B to C
4 Which family lives at Hatfield House, east of Junctions B and C?
5 Which monarch heard the news of her accession to the throne at Hatfield Palace?

Junctions C to D
6 The British Aerospace factory at Hatfield formerly belonged to De Havilland, the famous makers of light aeroplanes. Who was the first airwoman to fly solo from England to Australia?

Junctions D to E
7 Which well-known dramatist and essayist lived at Ayot St Lawrence, west of the motorway?
8 Queen Elizabeth the Queen Mother was born in St Paul's Walden, west of Stevenage. What was her maiden name?
9 What is the name of the Queen Mother's Scottish home near John O'Groats?
10 Junction E leads into Stevenage, where the novelist E.M. Forster spent his childhood. Which two of his novels have recently been filmed?

Junctions E to F

11 Shortly before Junction F the motorway crosses the main line north from Kings Cross. Who designed the *Flying Scotsman*, and on what date did she haul the first non-stop train from London to Edinburgh?

12 Shirley Williams was formerly MP for Hitchin, west of Junction F. What was the last Cabinet post she held?

Junctions F to G

13 The founder members of the Social Democratic Party were nicknamed the 'Gang of Four'. Who were they?

14 Letchworth, laid out in 1903, was the first garden city. Who founded the garden city movement?

Junctions G to H

15 From Junction H the A1 leads north towards Huntingdon and Peterborough. Which seventeenth-century military and political leader was born in Huntingdon?

16 What successful television dramatization of a Victorian novel was filmed in and around the precincts of Peterborough Cathedral?

17 In which newspaper does a column appear under the pseudonym Peterborough?

A1(M) YORKSHIRE

Junctions A to B

18 The famous scientist Isaac Newton was born near Grantham and went to school there. What were his three celebrated scientific achievements?

19 On its way north, the A1 passes through Newark, which has given its name to a major city in the USA. In which state is this American Newark?

20 Newark was besieged three times during the English Civil War. Whose side did the townspeople take?

21 The village of Tickhill, now close to the motorway, was licensed for tourneys by Richard I. What was a tourney?

Junctions B to C

22 The twelfth-century keep at Conisbrough Castle, west of the motorway, is one of the finest in the country. What was the medieval name for the lavatories that were let into castle walls?

Junctions C to D

23 The St Leger takes place every September at Doncaster Racecourse. When was the race first run, and over what distance is it run?

24 The *Luttrell Psalter*, now in the British Museum, was commissioned by Sir Geoffrey Luttrell, whose family came from Hooton Pagnell, east of the motorway. What is a psalter?

Junctions D to E

25 Further north, the A1 runs just west of the site of the Battle of Marston Moor. Who commanded the forces on each side?

26 To the east, on the far side of York, is the site of another battle, Stamford Bridge. When did this battle take place, and who defeated whom?

A1(M)   THE NORTH-EAST

Junctions A to B

27 This section of motorway starts a few miles north of Richmond, where a mathematician called Charles Lutwidge Dodgson went to school. By what name is he better known?

28 Captain James Cook was born at the edge of the North York Moors some miles east of the motorway. What were the names of the two ships he took on his final voyage of exploration?

29 Where is Cook Strait?

Junctions B to C

30 Junction B leads east to Darlington and Stockton. By what name was the first Lord Stockton better known?

31 Where does the river Tees rise?

Junctions C to D

32 Between these junctions the motorway crosses the Darlington to Bishop Auckland railway, which runs on the route of the original Stockton & Darlington line. Which was the first locomotive to operate on the line, and who built it?

Junctions D to E

33 When did the Stockton & Darlington line open?

34 Which locomotive engineer was put in charge of the Stockton & Darlington's repair shop at Shildon, two stations up the line?

35 Who wrote the novel *Whisky Galore*?

Junctions E to F

36 Crook is a small town west of the motorway. What is the origin of the term 'by hook or by crook'?

37 When and where was the word 'crook' first used to mean a professional criminal?

38 Junction F leads east to Peterlee. After whom is the town named?

39 The motorway is now running through County Durham, which has always been one of the strongholds of the British Labour movement. When was the Labour Party founded, and under what name?

Junctions F to G

40 Who was the first Labour Cabinet Minister?

41 When and where was the Trades Union Congress founded?

42 Junction G leads to Durham City. When is the annual miners' gala held?

Junctions G to H

43 Durham University, founded in 1832, was the third university created in England. Which were the first two, and which was the fourth?

44 Who wrote the *Ecclesiastical History of the English Nation*?

45 On which river does Durham stand?

46 What used to be manufactured at Consett, west of the motorway?

Junctions H to J

47 Junction H leads east to Sunderland. In which years did Sunderland win the FA Cup, and what was the score?

Junction J to Washington-Birtley Services

48 Washington new town takes its name from the ancestors of George Washington, who lived here between the twelfth and fourteenth centuries. Who succeeded Washington as President of the USA?

Washington-Birtley Services to Junction K

49 What is the capital of the state of Washington in the USA?

Junctions K to L

50 When are the US presidential elections held?

Junctions L to M

51 The athlete Brendan Foster trained at Gateshead Athletics Club, north-west of the motorway. What are the club's colours?

Junctions M to N

52 *Robinson Crusoe* is said to have been written in Gateshead. Who wrote the story, and what name did he give to Crusoe's companion on the desert island?

M1

Junctions 1 to 2
53 The Royal Aircraft Museum and the Battle of Britain Museum are just west of the motorway. Which two bodies amalgamated to form the RAF, and when?

Junction 2 to Scratchwood Services
54 Which day is celebrated each year as Battle of Britain Day?
55 Which railway company built the main line that runs alongside the motorway, and when was it opened?

Scratchwood Services to Junction 4
56 Which twentieth-century Prime Ministers were educated at Harrow School, a few miles west of the motorway?

Junctions 4 to 5
57 Shortly after Junction 4, the motorway crosses into Hertfordshire from Greater London. In which year did the Greater London Council come into being, and when was it abolished?
58 Who was the last leader of the Greater London Council?
59 Which television company has studios at Elstree?

Junctions 5 to 6
60 Elton John is chairman of Watford Football Club. Which was his first song to enter the hit parade?

Junctions 6 to 6a
61 Abbots Langley is a short distance west of the motorway. What position does an abbot hold?

Junctions 6a to 7
62 Which English monarch was captured at the first Battle of St Albans and deposed after the second?

Junctions 7 to 8
63 The municipal district based on Hemel Hempstead, reached from Junction 8, is known as Dacorum. What does the word Dacorum mean?

Junctions 8 to 9

64 At Junction 9 the motorway crosses the Roman road known as Watling Street. Which two Roman cities did it connect?

65 Junction 9 is the exit for Whipsnade Zoo, where both Dromedaries and Bactrian Camels can be seen. What is the main difference between the two species, and where does each originate?

Junctions 9 to 10

66 Which is the largest terrestrial carnivore in the world?

67 Which is the tallest living mammal in the world?

Junctions 10 to 11

68 You have just crossed the border into Bedfordshire. What is a Bedfordshire Clanger?

69 The motorway is now running west of Luton. In which year did Luton reach the Cup Final, and what was the score?

Junction 11 to Toddington Services

70 What type of clothing was Luton once famous for making?

71 The railway line from London to Sheffield runs immediately east of the motorway. To which gauge are almost all railway lines in Great Britain built?

Toddington Services to Junction 12

72 How many portions of chips are served each week at the Toddington Service Station?

73 How many coaches stop at Toddington Service Station each year?

Junctions 12 to 13

74 Sir Joseph Paxton, the gardener turned architect who designed the Crystal Palace, was born in the little village of Milton Bryan, just west of the motorway. For what event was the Crystal Palace built?

75 Which family owns Woburn Abbey, a few miles west of the motorway?

76 Woburn Abbey has an especially fine collection of works by Canaletto. From which city did this painter come?

77 Junction 13 is the main exit for Bedford. Which celebrated writer of religious works was imprisoned in the town jail for twelve years?

78   Who was Henry VIII's first wife, and for how long were they married?

Junctions 13 to 14

79   Now the motorway is running near the new town of Milton Keynes. How many kilometres of road are there in the city?

80   Coca-Cola runs a factory at Milton Keynes. Approximately how many cans of Coca-Cola are drunk each year in Great Britain: 1 million, 100 million or 1,000 million?

81   Which academic institution has its headquarters at Milton Keynes?

Junction 14 to Newport Pagnell Services

82   Chicheley Hall, east of the motorway at Junction 14, is owned by descendants of Admiral Beatty. Which World War One battle, in which Beatty took a decisive part, resulted in the German fleet staying in harbour for the rest of the war?

Newport Pagnell Services to Junction 15

83   Where does the river Ouse, which the motorway crosses north of the service station, reach the sea?

84   Apart from the Great Ouse, how many river Ouses are there in England?

85   Olney lies 4 miles east of the motorway. Which eighteenth-century poet and hymn-writer made his home there?

86   The Olney Pancake Race is run every Shrove Tuesday. Why are pancakes traditionally eaten on Shrove Tuesday?

87   Savoury and sweet pancakes are a speciality of Britanny. By what name are pancakes known in France?

88   To the west of the motorway, the Grand Union Canal runs through Blisworth Tunnel. How did canal barges travel through tunnels before engines were invented?

Junction 15 to Rothersthorpe Services

89   Between Junctions 15 and 16 the motorway runs west of Northampton. Which comedian might have started his career playing for Northampton Town Football Club but became a Butlin's Redcoat instead?

90   Which river flows through Northampton?

91   Which Northampton schoolboy played the title role in the TV adaptation of *The Secret Diary of Adrian Mole Aged 13¾*?

92   Boots and shoes are an important Northamptonshire industry. What name is given to the model of a foot on which boots and shoes are made?

Rothersthorpe Services to Junction 16
93   What are clogs?
94   Which English monarch was captured at the Battle of Northampton in 1460?

Junction 16 to Watford Gap Services
95   Where is the family home of the Earls of Spencer?
96   What are the full names of the two children of the Prince and Princess of Wales, and when were they born?
97   Who built the London & Birmingham Railway, which runs alongside the motorway near the service station, and when did it open?
98   What was the name of the experimental train British Rail developed during the 1970s, but never put into general service, and what was its special feature?

Watford Gap Services to Junction 17
99   How far is Watford Gap from Watford?

Junctions 17 to 18
100   Rugby lies west of the motorway at Junction 18. Which celebrated nineteenth-century novel was set at Rugby School?

Junctions 18 to 19
101   Who wrote these lines:
   'If I should die, think only this of me
   That there's some corner of a foreign field
   That is for ever England'?
102   The motorway crosses the Upper Avon river just south of Junction 19. What is the origin of the word Avon?

Junctions 19 to 20
103   Stanford Hall, east of the motorway, contains a museum commemorating Percy Pilcher, a pioneer British glider pilot killed in 1899. Who made the world's first genuine powered flight, when, and what was the plane called?
104   Who was the first person to fly across the English Channel?
105   Who was the first person to translate the Bible into English?

Junctions 20 to 21

106 The motorway is now running through Leicestershire. Several Leicestershire place names include the word Ashby – for instance, Ashby Parva and Ashby Magna, east and west of the motorway. What is the origin of the word Ashby?

107 With which county was Leicestershire merged in 1974?

108 Where is Stilton cheese made?

109 With which drink is Stilton traditionally served?

110 The Battle of Bosworth was fought near Sutton Cheney in west Leicestershire. Which war did it conclude, and when did it take place?

111 Which king was killed in the Battle of Bosworth, and which dynasty came to the throne as a result?

Junction 21 to Leicester Forest East Services

112 Junctions 21 and 22 are the exits for Leicester. On which river does Leicester stand?

113 Which Leicester man organized the first railway excursion in 1841, and went on to found a world-famous travel company?

Leicester Forest East Services to Junction 22

114 Which Leicester author wrote *The Secret Diary of Adrian Mole Aged 13¾*?

115 What is the name of the Roman road that runs through Leicester?

116 Cardinal Wolsey died at Leicester in 1530. Where was the grand country residence he built himself outside London?

117 Who was known as the 'Nine-Day Queen'?

118 Herds of fallow and red deer roam in Bradgate Park, east of the motorway. What names are given to the male, female and young of each species?

Junctions 22 to 23

119 Beacon Hill lies about 1½ miles east of the motorway. If you travelled east from there, where would you find land as high?

120 What are belisha beacons, and after whom are they named?

121 For which sport is the village of Quorn, east of the motorway, well known?

Junctions 23 to 24

122 The former Great Central Railway ran through Loughborough. What was its London terminus?

123 Loughborough's industry includes a well-known bell foundry. What word is used to describe the science of bells and bell-ringing?

124 Junction 24 is the exit for the East Midlands Airport and Donington Park Circuit. What term is used to describe a queue of planes waiting to land at an airport?

125 Which team from which country won the 1937 and 1938 British Grand Prix races held at Donington Park?

Junctions 24 to 25

126 Between these junctions the motorway crosses the river Trent and the Nottingham to Derby railway. How long is the Trent, and through how many counties does it flow?

127 Which Yorkshire linen-draper turned railway magnate formed the Midland Railway?

128 Junction 25 leads to Derby and Nottingham. When and where is the Derby run, and for which horses?

129 Who has managed both Derby County and Nottingham Forest Football Clubs?

Junction 25 to Trowell Services

130 Which national chain of chemists has its headquarters in Nottingham?

131 Which Nottingham man founded the Salvation Army?

Trowell Services to Junction 26

132 Who won the gold for Ice Dancing at the 1984 Olympic Games?

Junctions 26 to 27

133 Which sport is played at Trent Bridge, Nottingham?

134 The novelist D.H. Lawrence was born at Eastwood, west of the motorway at Junction 26. Of which novel are Ursula and Gudrun Brangwen the heroines?

135 Who was Lady Chatterley's lover?

136 Who robbed the rich to help the poor in Sherwood Forest, north of Nottingham?

137 What job did a sheriff have in the Middle Ages?

Junctions 27 to 28

138 The poet Byron's family home was at Newstead Abbey, east of Junction 27. Where did Byron die, and in what cause?

139 Who, in Byron's words, was 'butcher'd to make a Roman holiday'?

Junctions 28 to 29

140 North of Junction 28, the motorway crosses the East Midlands coalfield. How many tonnes of coal were mined in Great Britain in 1985–86?

141 Why were canaries formerly carried underground after an explosion or fire in a mine?

142 Among the treasures at Hardwick Hall, visible east of the motorway south of Junction 29, are tapestries depicting the story of Hero and Leander. Who were Hero and Leander?

143 Bess of Hardwick built Hardwick Hall. Her great-grandson was the 1st Duke of Devonshire. Which well-known Derbyshire house did he build?

Junctions 29 to 30

144 North of Junction 29, Bolsover Castle is visible on a ridge east of the motorway. What were the two main features of the earliest Norman castles built in England?

145 George Stephenson lived for many years at Chesterfield, a short distance west of the motorway. Apart from his work on steam locomotives, for what other invention is he famous?

146 What does a Chesterfield settee look like?

147 What is a Chesterfield coat?

148 Chesterfield is well known for its leaning church spire. Where else in Europe is there a celebrated leaning tower?

Junction 30 to Woodall Services

149 Sailing and archery are popular sports at the Rother Valley Country Park west of the motorway. What are the proper terms for the left and right sides of a boat, and for the front and back ends?

Woodall Services to Junction 31

150 What are the colours of the central circle and the four outer concentric bands on the target face used in archery, and what are their scoring values?

151 A tiny village called Wales lies west of the motorway. What is the Welsh word for Wales?

Junctions 31 to 32

152   The motorway has now entered Yorkshire. Into how many ridings was the county formerly divided?

Junctions 32 to 33

153   Who wrote the novel *South Riding*?

Junctions 33 to 34

154   Between Junctions 33 and 35 the motorway runs along the eastern edge of Sheffield. What product was first manufactured in Sheffield in the fourteenth century, and is still made there today?

155   What did Benjamin Huntsman first make in Sheffield in 1742?

156   The English river Don, which the motorway crosses at Junction 33, is 70 miles long. How long is the river Don in the USSR, and into which sea does it flow?

Junctions 34 to 35

157   Who was imprisoned in the now demolished Sheffield Castle for 14 years in the sixteenth century?

158   What is the Sheffield Shield?

159   Where was HMS *Sheffield* sunk, and what was the missile that destroyed her?

Junctions 35 to 36

160   You are now in the heart of Yorkshire. Which Yorkshire cricketer has taken more Test Match wickets than any other player?

161   Which Yorkshire cricketer has scored more runs in Test Matches and batted for longer in Tests than any other player?

Junctions 36 to 37

162   Worsbrough Mill is a water-powered corn mill preserved as a museum, north of Junction 36. How is grain ground in a mill?

163   Barnsley lies east of Junction 37. Which railway engineer, educated in the town, built the line over Shap and Beattock summits between Lancashire and Glasgow, among many other routes?

164   Which TV and radio chat show star and cricket enthusiast comes from Barnsley?

165   Who was sitting on Barnsley railway station, with a 'ticket for his destination'?

Junctions 37 to 38

166 The Yorkshire coalfield was one of the strongest centres of the miners' strike in 1984–5. How long did the strike last, and how many working days were lost?

167 Who is President of the National Union of Mineworkers?

168 The TV series *Last of the Summer Wine* was filmed at Holmfirth, west of the motorway. What were the names of the three principal original characters?

Junction 38 to Woolley Edge Services

169 The Granada Group, which owns Woolley Edge Services, also runs a TV station based in Manchester. One of its most famous programmes is *Coronation Street*. When was the first episode broadcast, and who took the parts of Ena Sharples and Albert Tatlock?

Woolley Edge Services to Junction 39

170 *Brideshead Revisited* was another very successful Granada programme. Who wrote the original novel, and which playwright adapted it for the screen?

171 In Granada's adaptation of *Brideshead Revisited*, who played the parts of Sebastian Flyte, his sister Julia, and Charles Ryder, and who was Aloysius?

Junctions 39 to 40

172 Junctions 39, 40 and 41 all lead into Wakefield. Who lost his life at the Battle of Wakefield in 1460?

173 Which Wakefield-born sculptor died in a fire at her home in St Ives in 1975?

Junctions 40 to 41

174 The Wakefield Mystery Plays are one of the four surviving cycles of mystery or miracle plays. What were mystery plays?

175 Which Wakefield-born novelist wrote *New Grub Street* and *The Private Papers of Henry Ryecroft* among many other works?

Junctions 41 to 42

176 Bowls is a popular Yorkshire sport. Each player delivers a number of bowls towards a smaller white ball. What name is given to the bowls and to the smaller ball?

Junctions 42 to 43

177 The motorway is now approaching the centre of Leeds. Which river flows through the city?

Junctions 43 to 47

178 Who was manager of Leeds United when they were League Champions in 1969 and 1974?

179 What sports are played at the Headingley ground in Leeds?

M11

Junctions 3 to 4
180 The motorway starts in north-east London, a few miles north of the West Ham United Football ground. What was West Ham's original name?

Junctions 4 to 5
181 The poet, artist and craftsman William Morris was born at Walthamstow, west of Junction 4. What was the name of the private press he established at Hammersmith in 1890?
182 Grange Hill lies east of the motorway, Woodford to the west. Who writes the scripts for the BBC TV serial *Grange Hill*?
183 Who was MP for Woodford until he retired from Parliament in 1964?

Junctions 5 to 6
184 Epping Forest, to the west of the motorway, is partly in Greater London, and partly in Essex. Which London Borough includes part of the Forest?
185 The motorway is now running through Essex. Which town is the county town of Essex?

Junctions 6 to 7
186 Halfway between Junctions 6 and 7, the Epping to Ongar branch of the Central Line crosses the motorway. How many stations are there on the London underground system, and which is the busiest?
187 What was the nickname given to the Central Line when it opened in 1900?
188 The terminus of the Central Line is at Chipping Ongar, a few miles east. What does the word Chipping mean?
189 The explorer David Livingstone trained for the ministry in Ongar. Who was sent to look for Livingstone in Africa, and by which newspaper?

Junctions 7 to 8
190 Junction 7 leads into Harlow, one of the eight new towns planned around London after 1945. Which are the other seven?

191 What were New Towns for?

192 Who was the original Blonde Bombshell?

193 Queen Mary I lived for much of her childhood at Hunsdon, west of Harlow. Whom did she marry?

194 Dick Whittington was once Lord of the Manor at Thorley, a small village west of the motorway. Which church bells chimed as, according to legend, he was leaving London, and what did they promise him?

Junctions 8 to 9

195 Bishop's Stortford is just west of the motorway at Junction 8. How did the town get its name?

196 Cecil Rhodes, the founder of Rhodesia, was born at Bishop's Stortford. Who was the last white Prime Minister of Rhodesia, and by what name is the country now known?

197 Great and Little Dunmow lie east of Junction 8. What is the Dunmow Flitch?

198 Stansted Airport has been designated London's third airport. How many passengers are planned to use the airport by the mid-1990s?

199 North of Stansted, the motorway runs close to the river Cam. By what other name is the Cam known?

200 Audley End House and Saffron Walden lie a short distance east of the motorway about two-thirds of the way between Junctions 8 and 9. The grounds of Audley End were laid out by 'Capability' Brown. What was his real first name, and how did he come by his nickname?

201 Saffron Walden takes its name from the saffron grown in the area from the fifteenth to the eighteenth centuries. For what was saffron used?

202 Dick Turpin, the celebrated highwayman, was born at Hempstead, east of Saffron Walden. What was his first job, before he turned to crime?

203 The physician William Harvey is buried in Hempstead. For what medical discovery is he famous?

Junctions 9 to 10

204 Ickleton, close to Junction 9, stands on the prehistoric track that ran from East Anglia to the South Midlands. What is this route called?

205 Junction 10 leads to Newmarket, headquarters of the turf. When was the first recorded race held at Newmarket, and why is the mile-long course known as the Rowley Mile?

206 Which two classic races are run at Newmarket at the start of the racing season?

Junctions 10 to 11
207 Among the aircraft on show at the Imperial War Museum's collection at Duxford are the B–17 and the B–29. By what names are these two planes known?
208 For what is the B–29 *Enola Gay* famous?
209 Why are the Gog Magog Hills, visible east of the motorway, so called?

Junctions 11 to 12
210 Between Junctions 11 and 14 the motorway runs east of Cambridge. Where is the annual Boat Race between Oxford and Cambridge Universities rowed?
211 What two questions in his poem *The Old Vicarage, Grantchester* did the poet Rupert Brooke ask about Grantchester, east of the motorway?

Junctions 12 to 13
212 Which Cambridge College did Prince Edward attend?

Junctions 13 to 14
213 Which monarch founded King's College, Cambridge?

M18

Junction 32 (M1) to Junction 1

214 Roche Abbey, east of the motorway, was a Cistercian foundation. From what monastic order did the first Cistercian monks break away?

215 Where was the first Cistercian monastery founded?

Junctions 1 to 2

216 The motorway is now running through the county of South Yorkshire. Which cleric wrote 'My living in Yorkshire was so far out of the way, that it was actually twelve miles from a lemon'?

217 What is a 'yorker'?

218 How many universities are there in Yorkshire?

Junctions 2 to 3

219 Between Junctions 2 and 4, the motorway runs south and east of Doncaster. What was the name of the Roman settlement there?

220 What is the first major horse race of the flat season?

Junctions 3 to 4

221 The Mansion House in Doncaster is one of the most attractive houses in the town. What is London's Mansion House used for?

222 The east-coast main line through Doncaster is currently being electrified. What is the name of the arm that takes power from the overhead wire to the locomotive?

223 Which railway company opened its locomotive and carriage works at Doncaster in 1851?

224 Sir Nigel Gresley became locomotive engineer at Doncaster in 1911. Which Class were his famous streamlined Pacific locomotives?

Junctions 4 to 5

225 In which year did British Rail operate its last regular steam-hauled services?

226 Yorkshire is a well-known cricketing county. What are the county's colours?

Junctions 5 to 6

227 In which year was the Yorkshire County Cricket Club founded?

Junctions 6 to 7

228 What are the Ashes?

229 Shortly before the end of the motorway the boundary between South Yorkshire and Humberside is crossed. How many counties are there in England?

M180

Junctions 1 to 2

230 A few miles from the start of the motorway you enter Humberside, whose two parts, north and south of the river, are linked by the Humber Bridge. How much did the bridge cost to build?

231 The Humber bridge was opened in 1981. When was the decision to build it announced, and what was happening in the area at the time?

232 Charles and John Wesley lived at Epworth, south of the motorway. Which Church did they found?

233 To which well-known Christmas carol did Charles Wesley write the words?

234 Until 1974, this area was part of Lincolnshire. Lincoln Cathedral is the third largest cathedral in England. Which two cathedrals are larger?

Junctions 2 to 3

235 Of which party was President Lincoln of the USA a member?

236 Which celebrated Victorian poet was born in Somersby, Lincolnshire?

237 Gainsborough, south of the motorway, has no connection with the eighteenth-century portrait painter Thomas Gainsborough. Where was he born?

Junctions 3 to 4

238 Which controversial cricketer has also played football for Scunthorpe United?

239 Which ex-captains of the England football team once played for Scunthorpe?

240 Which English artist published a monumental work entitled *Anatomy of the Horse* in 1766?

241 What is the name of the Roman road that crosses the motorway at Junction 4?

Junctions 4 to 5

242 Brigg is just south of the motorway between Junctions 4 and 5. Who composed the orchestral work *Brigg Fair*?

243 What is a brig?

244 A range of low hills is visible south-east of the end of the motorway. What are they called?

245 Which Lincolnshire resort made a name for itself by advertising its bracing climate?

M2

Junctions 1 to 2

246 The motorway starts near Gad's Hill, where the novelist Charles Dickens lived for the last fourteen years of his life. Which four novels did he write there?

247 Just after Junction 2, the motorway crosses the Medway, where it can be very windy. On which scale is wind speed measured, and how is a storm described?

Junctions 2 to 3

248 What happened in the Medway in June 1667?

249 Which monarch established the naval base at Chatham?

250 Which celebrated ship was launched at Chatham dockyard in 1765?

Junctions 3 to 4

251 Who was created the 1st Earl of Chatham?

252 Junction 4 leads into Gillingham. Which military formation has its headquarters in the town?

Junction 4 to Farthing Corner Services

253 Which television entertainer and presenter supported Gillingham Football Club as a young boy?

Farthing Corner Services to Junction 5

254 The motorway is now running through the heart of Kent. Which Kentish cricketer has appeared in more Tests than any other English cricketer?

255 How many catches did Frank Woolley take in his 32-year career playing for Kent?

Junctions 5 to 6

256 There are clear views across to the Isle of Sheppey between these junctions. What is the name of the channel that separates the island from the mainland?

257 What does the name Sheppey mean?

258 After which queen is Queenborough on the west of the Isle of Sheppey named?

259 Junction 6 leads into Faversham. Which monarch was held prisoner for several days at Faversham after trying to flee to France?

260 Bob Geldof lives near Faversham. Which honour did he receive in 1986?

261 What was the name of Band Aid's hit song in December 1984?

Junctions 6 to 7

262 After the end of the motorway, the A299 runs into Whitstable, the A2 to Canterbury and Dover. For which seafood is Whitstable renowned?

263 Which archbishop of Canterbury was murdered in his cathedral, and which twentieth-century dramatist wrote a play about the event?

264 Who wrote the poem *Dover Beach*?

M20

Junctions 1 to 2

265 The motorway starts a short distance past the boundary between Greater London and Kent. Which town is the county town of Kent?

266 Which British monarch was the only child of a Duke and Duchess of Kent?

267 Who are the children of the present Duke and Duchess of Kent?

268 Brands Hatch lies just west of the motorway about halfway between Junctions 1 and 2. How long is the Grand Prix circuit there?

269 What sort of flag is displayed to signal the end of a Grand Prix race?

270 New Ash Green, east of the motorway, is an experimental twentieth-century village. Which company built it?

Junctions 2 to 3

271 Near Junction 2, the motorway crosses the Pilgrims' Way. Which places does the path connect, and how did it come by its name?

Junctions 3 to 4

272 How many pilgrims appear in Chaucer's *Canterbury Tales*?

273 Trottiscliffe is a small village north of the motorway. How is its name pronounced?

Junctions 4 to 5

274 The motorway runs north of Maidstone between Junctions 5 and 7. Which Maidstone-born man led the Peasants' Revolt?

275 One of Maidstone's attractions is the Tyrwhitt-Drake Museum of Carriages. What is a sedan chair?

276 The Carriage Museum is housed in a former tithe barn. What was a tithe barn?

Junctions 5 to 6

277 Between these junctions the motorway crosses the river Medway. How long is the Medway?

Junctions 6 to 7
278 What is the difference between a Man of Kent and a Kentish Man?

Junctions 7 to 8
279 Between these junctions the motorway crosses the Maidstone to Ashford railway line. On what system were the lines of the old Southern Railway electrified?

280 Leeds Castle is just off the A20, a short distance from Junction 8. After whom is the castle named?

Junctions 9 to 10
281 Who was Britain's first woman novelist?

Junctions 10 to 11
282 What is Kentish rag?

283 South of the motorway is Romney Marsh, through which the Royal Military Canal runs. Which places does the Canal link, and why was it built?

284 On what gauge is the Romney, Hythe and Dymchurch Railway built?

285 Who wrote *The Railway Children*?

Junctions 11 to 12
286 Junction 11 leads into Hythe, one of the Cinque Ports. Which are the other four?

287 Who currently holds the office of Lord Warden of the Cinque Ports?

288 The celebrated art historian Kenneth Clark lived at Saltwood Castle, between Junctions 11 and 12. Which television programme brought him public acclaim?

Junctions 12 to 13
289 The motorway ends on the outskirts of Folkestone, which is one of the main Channel ports. Where is the narrowest point of the Channel, and how wide is it there?

290 What is the French name for the English Channel?

M23

Junctions 7 to 8

291 The motorway starts a short distance into Surrey from Greater London. Where is the headquarters of the Surrey County Cricket Club, and from which organization is its ground leased?

Junctions 8 to 9

292 How many runs did Jack Hobbs score in his 29-year career playing for Surrey?

293 Many travellers on the M23 are heading for Brighton. In which nineteenth-century novel is Brighton described as 'the place to get husbands'?

294 What was Brighton called in the early nineteenth century?

295 Who designed Brighton Pavilion?

296 According to tradition, the glow of the Fire of London could be seen from the hill-top village of Outwood, east of the motorway. In which street did the Fire start, and where did it finish?

Junctions 9 to 10

297 Gatwick Airport, reached from Junction 9, is London's second airport. How many destinations are served by scheduled services from Gatwick?

298 How many signs are there in the Gatwick Airport complex?

299 Meteorologists define thick fog as visibility of less than 20 metres. On average, how many hours of thick fog are there each year at Gatwick, and which are the most and least foggy months?

Junctions 10 to 11

300 The motorway finishes at the delightfully-named Pease Pottage. How did Pease Pottage come by its name?

M25

Junctions 1 to 2

301 What is the name of the new town being developed on Plumstead Marshes, a few miles upstream of the Dartford Tunnel?

Junctions 2 to 3

302 Who developed the first steam locomotives capable of hauling wagons?

303 Edward Heath is the MP for Bexley, a few miles west of the motorway. When was he Prime Minister, and who succeeded him as leader of the Conservative Party?

Junctions 3 to 4

304 The chapel at Lullingstone Roman Villa, east of the motorway, is one of the oldest places of Christian worship discovered in this country. By which Emperor was Christianity recognized throughout the Roman Empire?

305 At Lullingstone Castle the first game of lawn tennis is said to have been played. Which player has won more Wimbledon titles than any other player?

306 Which four tennis championships make up the Grand Slam?

Junction 4 to 5

307 The motorway is now running near the Darent Valley. Which nineteenth-century artist is closely associated with the area?

308 To which family did Knole, the magnificent stately mansion south of Sevenoaks, belong for 400 years?

Junctions 5 to 6

309 Who wrote *The Origin of Species*?

310 Westerham lies south of the motorway. Which famous military commander was born in the town?

311 What was the name of Winston Churchill's country home south of Westerham?

312 After many years in the political wilderness, Churchill was recalled to office in 1939. What post was he given?

313 What phrase did Churchill coin in a celebrated speech at Fulton, Missouri, USA, in March 1946, and what did it describe?

314 RAF Biggin Hill, north of the motorway, played a vital role in the defence of London during the blitz. How many tons of high explosives were dropped in night attacks on London during the blitz?

Junctions 6 to 7

315 The Pepys family came from Tandridge, now south of the motorway at Junction 6. To what government post was Samuel Pepys appointed in 1672?

316 Who compiled the new English prayer-book authorized by Edward VI?

Junctions 7 to 8

317 The North Downs Way long-distance path runs close to the motorway. Which places are at each end of the path?

318 Who led the English fleet that defeated the Spanish Armada?

Junctions 8 to 9

319 Dorking lies south-west of the motorway after Junction 9. Which river flows through the town?

320 Which Dorking-born economist put forward the theory that the population tends to increase faster than the means of subsistence?

321 Epsom lies a few miles north of the motorway. What is the medicinal use of Epsom Salts?

322 Apart from the Derby, which are the two best-known races run at Epsom race-course?

323 The theatre at Leatherhead, close to Junction 9, is named after the actress Dame Sybil Thorndike. What was the name of her husband, also an actor?

Junctions 9 to 10

324 Sybil Thorndike and her husband wrote a biography of Lilian Baylis, the theatrical manager. With which two London theatres was Lilian Baylis closely connected?

325 Which exiled European monarch moved to Claremont, now a few miles north of the motorway, in 1848?

326 What was the name of the Prince Regent's daughter?

327 Which celebrated multi-millionaire lived at Sutton Place, a few miles west along the A3 from Junction 10?

Junctions 10 to 11

328 Brooklands closed-circuit race track, near Weybridge, was famous for motor-racing between 1907 and 1939. It was also the cradle of British aviation. Who was the first Englishman to construct and fly his own plane?

329 The Shah Jehan Mosque at Woking, west of the motorway, is a major centre of Islam in Britain. Who founded the Islamic religion, and what is the name of its holy book?

330 What is the Hajj?

Junctions 11 to 12

331 Which monarch was buried in the Benedictine monastery at Chertsey, close to Junction 11?

Junctions 12 to 13

332 Who lived at Fort Belvedere, between Virginia Water and Sunningdale, during the 1930s?

333 Which American president is commemorated at Runnymede?

Junctions 13 to 14

334 The motorway is now running close to Heathrow Airport. How many cups of tea and coffee are sold at Heathrow every day?

Junctions 14 to 15

335 How much liquor is sold at the duty-free shops in the airport each year?

336 The headquarters of Penguin Books was formerly at Harmondsworth, east of Junction 15. Who founded the company?

Junctions 15 to 16

337 Which was the first Penguin book published, and when did it appear?

338 The London suburbs to the east of the motorway are part of the London Borough of Hillingdon. How many London boroughs are there?

339 Which poem is said to have been composed in Stoke Poges churchyard, west of the motorway?

340 Which contemporary playwright made his name with a play based on the off-stage adventures of two characters in *Hamlet*?

Junctions 16 to 17
341 Chalfont St Peter is a short distance west of the motorway. What is St Peter usually depicted holding?

342 Captain James Cook was a frequent visitor to Chalfont St Giles, a few miles further north. Where was he killed?

343 For what sort of operations has Harefield Hospital, a few miles east of the motorway, become well known in recent years?

Junctions 17 to 18
344 Three rivers meet in Rickmansworth, east of these junctions. What are their names?

Junctions 18 to 19
345 Junction 19 leads into Watford. Whom did Watford play in the 1984 Cup Final, and what was the score?

346 The M25 is the London Orbital motorway. What is the population of Greater London?

Junctions 19 to 20
347 Through how many counties does the M25 pass, and what are they?

Junctions 20 to 21
348 Who wrote 'When a man is tired of London, he is tired of life; for there is in London all that life can afford'?

349 Who wrote 'Hell is a city much like London'?

Junctions 21 to 22
350 Who was the only Englishman to become Pope?

Junctions 22 to 23
351 The motorway is now running a few miles south of St Albans. What did the Romans call the city?

352 In AD 61, the first Roman settlement here was sacked by Boudicca. Who was Boudicca?

353 Who was Alban?

Junctions 23 to 24

354 North of Junction 22, at London Colney, is the Mosquito Aircraft Museum. What was the nickname of the De Havilland Mosquito, and what was its top speed?

355 Barnet lies south of the motorway. What is the origin of the name Barnet?

356 Who was killed at the Battle of Barnet in 1471?

357 For much of its route, the M25 runs through the Green Belt. What is the Green Belt?

Junctions 24 to 25

358 Of which tube line is Cockfosters, south of the motorway, the northern terminus?

359 About halfway between Junctions 24 and 25 the motorway runs north of a hamlet known as Botany Bay. Where else is there a Botany Bay?

360 Who wrote *London Labour and the London Poor*?

361 Junction 25 leads to Waltham Cross and Theobald's Park. The cross at Waltham Cross is known as an Eleanor Cross. Whom do Eleanor Crosses commemorate?

Junctions 25 to 26

362 Since the late nineteenth century, Temple Bar has stood in Theobald's Park. Where was it originally erected, and what did it mark?

363 Soon after Junction 25, the motorway crosses the river Lea. Where does the Lea join the Thames?

364 Which monarch is said to have been buried in Waltham Abbey?

Junctions 26 to 27

365 Near Waltham Abbey, the motorway crosses the Greenwich Meridian. In what year was it agreed internationally that the Greenwich Meridian should be the zero or prime meridian?

366 Through which two other European countries does the Greenwich Meridian pass?

367 The motorway is now running through the northern edge of Epping Forest. Who administers the Forest?

Junctions 27 to 28

368 The motorway is now running through Essex. What was the principal military triumph of Robert Devereux, 2nd Earl of Essex?

369 Where and why was Robert Devereux executed?

370 The royal palace at Havering-atte-Bower south of the motorway was the official residence of England's queens, including the first three wives of Henry VIII. What were they called, and what happened to them?

371 Amstrad Consumer Electronics has its head office at Brentwood, close to Junction 28. What does AMSTRAD stand for?

372 On which arithmetical system do computers operate?

Junctions 28 to 29

373 These junctions both lead to Romford, which is well known for its brewery. How many gallons of beer make up a barrel?

374 At Junction 29 the motorway meets the A127, which leads east to Southend. How long is Southend Pier?

Junctions 29 to 30

375 Upminster, west of the motorway, is the eastern end of the District Line. How long does the journey to Ealing Broadway, the western terminus, take, and how many stations does the train pass through?

376 Geologists believe that Hornchurch, a short distance beyond Upminster, was at the furthest edge of the ice-sheet that covered England in the Ice Age. When was the last major phase of the Ice Age, and by what name is it known?

377 Construction of the Coalhouse Fort at Tilbury, east of the motorway, was supervised by Gordon of Khartoum. By what nickname was Gordon generally known in England?

Junctions 30 to 31

378 In which year were Tilbury Docks opened?

379 Junction 31 is the last chance to leave the motorway before crossing the Thames. Further upstream are the Ford works at Dagenham. How many people are employed there?

Junctions 31 to 1

380 London Bridge was for centuries the only bridge over the Thames in central London. Which was the second to be built?

381 The present London Bridge was built in the late 1960s. What happened to the previous one?

382 The Dartford Tunnel is the most recently opened tunnel under the Thames. How many other road tunnels are there under the river?

M27

Junctions 1 to 2
383 The motorway starts on the eastern edge of the New Forest. Which English monarch was killed while hunting in the New Forest?
384 How large is the New Forest, and which ancient body still controls grazing and other rights in the Forest?

Junctions 2 to 3
385 Which two rivers join to form Southampton Water?

Junction 3 to Rownhams Services
386 Who was the last Viceroy and the first Governor-General of India?

Rownhams Services to Junction 4
387 Between Junctions 3 and 7 the motorway runs north of Southampton. What is specially unusual about Southampton Water and the Solent?

Junctions 4 to 5
388 The *Titanic* sailed from Southampton on her maiden, and final, voyage. How many people went down with her?

Junctions 5 to 6
389 Which king of England is said to have commanded the waves to recede at Southampton, and why did he do so?

Junctions 6 to 7
390 Which celebrated aircraft first flew at Eastleigh, north of Junction 6, on 5 March 1936?
391 Which Southampton-born artist painted *The Boyhood of Raleigh*?

Junctions 7 to 8
392 The motorway runs a few miles inland from the Solent, on the far side of which lies the Isle of Wight. Which biennial yacht race starts at Cowes, and what route does it follow?

Junctions 8 to 9

393 Which royal couple made Osborne House, East Cowes, their home?

394 Most of the ships and men that took part in the D-Day invasion of France sailed from the Solent. What was the date of D-Day?

Junctions 9 to 10

395 What was the name given to the floating harbour designed to enable men and equipment to disembark in Normandy?

396 What sport flourished on Broadhalfpenny Down, Hambledon, a few miles north-west of the motorway, in the late eighteenth century?

Junctions 10 to 11

397 Portchester Castle can be seen on the coast just south of the motorway. Which king stayed here before leading his troops in the Battle of Agincourt?

398 The cranes of Portsmouth dockyard, where the *Mary Rose* and HMS *Victory* can be visited, are clearly visible. After whom was the *Mary Rose* named?

399 When did the *Mary Rose* sink, and how many men went down with her?

Junctions 11 to 12

400 What commission does HMS *Victory* currently hold?

401 What were Nelson's last words?

402 What is the nickname of Portsmouth Football Club?

M3

Junctions 1 to 2

403 The motorway starts at Sunbury, a few miles west of Twickenham and Hampton Court. Which sporting organization has its headquarters at Twickenham?

404 To whom did Hampton Court Palace originally belong?

405 The start of the motorway is in what was formerly the county of Middlesex. What is the original meaning of the name Middlesex?

406 Where is the headquarters of the Middlesex County Cricket Club?

Junctions 2 to 3

407 Ascot racecourse lies north of the motorway between Junctions 2 and 3. In which month is the Royal Meeting held each year, and what is the most prestigious race run during it?

408 One of the enclosures at Ascot and at many other racecourses is known as Tattersalls. Who or what are Tattersalls?

409 Bracknell, north of Junction 3, is the headquarters of the Meteorological Office. Who constructed the Centigrade thermometer, when, and what was his nationality?

410 What is lightning?

411 For what sport is Bisley, south of the motorway at Junction 3, well known?

Junctions 3 to 4

412 The Royal Military Academy, Sandhurst, to the north of the motorway, trains officers from both the United Kingdom and many other countries. Which two current heads of state passed through the College as officer cadets?

413 Samuel F. Cody achieved an important British first at Aldershot in 1908. What was it?

414 Which French Emperor who found refuge in England is buried in Farnborough?

Junction 4 to Fleet Services

415 When was the first military camp established at Aldershot?

416   Church Crookham, south of the motorway, is the home of the Gurkha Museum. From which country do Gurkhas come?

417   Who wrote *The Water Babies*?

Fleet Services to Junction 5

418   The motorway is now running through Hampshire. Where else besides Hampshire, according to the song in *My Fair Lady*, do hurricanes hardly ever happen?

419   On which stage play, by whom, is *My Fair Lady* based?

420   Hook is just north of the motorway at Junction 5. In which play does a character called Captain Hook appear?

Junctions 5 to 6

421   King John set out from Odiham Castle, just south of the motorway at Junction 5, to meet his barons and sign the *Magna Carta*. Where did the signing ceremony take place?

422   Greywell Tunnel, on the Basingstoke Canal, is the home of one of the largest colonies of bats in Britain. When, where and how do bats sleep?

423   Junction 6 leads to Basingstoke, where the Automobile Association has its head office. How many breakdown calls did the AA's patrols answer in 1985?

Junctions 6 to 7

424   In which Gilbert and Sullivan opera is the word Basingstoke said to teem with hidden meaning?

425   Steventon and Dummer are two villages close to Junction 7. Jane Austen was born at Steventon in 1775. In which of her novels does an unfortunate picnic take place at Box Hill, Surrey?

Junctions 7 to 8

426   Which daughter of a resident of Dummer married on 23 July 1986, and what title did she assume on that day?

Junctions 8 to 9

427   Which salad crop is extensively grown along the banks of streams in this part of Hampshire?

428   Which celebrated cricket commentator, writer and wine enthusiast lived at Alresford, east of the motorway, for many years?

429   Winchester lies at the end of the motorway. What name is given to the pupils of Winchester College?

430 St Swithin was Bishop of Winchester in the ninth century. When is St Swithin's Day and what, according to legend, will happen if it rains on that day?

431 Which Anglo-Saxon monarch is buried in Winchester Cathedral?

Junctions 9 to 10

432 Which group had a hit in the 1960s with *Winchester Cathedral*?

M4

Junctions 1 to 2
433 The motorway starts a short distance from the Thames and Kew Gardens. Which member of the royal family created the first botanic garden at Kew?

Junction 2 to Heston Services
434 Syon House stands on the opposite bank of the Thames from Kew. Which aristocratic family lives there?
435 Which rock singer was once an apprentice player with Brentford Football Club, a short distance south of the motorway?

Heston Services to Junction 3
436 Junction 3 is the exit for the Cargo Terminal at Heathrow Airport. How many tonnes of cargo are handled there each year?
437 How many creatures pass through the Quarantine Station at Heathrow each year?

Junctions 3 to 4
438 For the next few miles, you have a good view of aircraft taking off and landing at Heathrow. How many passengers use the airport each year, and how many different airlines?

Junctions 4 to 4a
439 When was the airport opened?

Junctions 4a to 5
440 The Grand Union Canal runs through Langley, north of the motorway. How did the canal-builders of the eighteenth century make their canal bottoms watertight?

Junctions 5 to 6
441 Junction 6 leads south to Eton and Windsor (the castle is visible from the motorway) and north to Slough. Who called for bombs to fall on Slough?
442 Which English monarch founded Eton College?
443 What was the name of the Duchess of Windsor before she married the Duke?

444 With which of his wives is Henry VIII buried in St George's Chapel, Windsor?

Junctions 6 to 7
445 Who lives in the Royal Lodge in Windsor Great Park?

Junctions 7 to 9
446 Between these junctions the motorway crosses the river Thames. How long is the Thames, and where is its source?

447 Who wrote the line 'Sweete Themmes runne softly, till I end my song'?

448 Jerome K. Jerome's novel *Three Men In A Boat* recounts the story of a boating holiday on the Thames. What were the names of the three travellers, and who came too?

Junctions 9 to 10
449 Cliveden House lies to the north of the motorway near Maidenhead. Which was the last aristocratic family to own it?

450 Henley lies a few miles to the north of the motorway between these junctions. When was the Henley Royal Regatta inaugurated, and how long is the course?

451 What is the full name of the person who steers an eight, and where does he or she sit?

452 Which well-known eighteenth-century poet lived at Binfield, near Wokingham, as a young man?

Junctions 10 to 11
453 Between Junctions 10 and 12 the motorway skirts Reading to the south. What food is the town well known for manufacturing?

454 Who wrote *The Ballad of Reading Gaol*?

455 Which English monarch died of a surfeit of lampreys in Normandy and was brought home to lie in Reading Abbey?

456 Which two rivers meet at Reading?

Junctions 11 to 12
457 Junction 11 leads south to Stratfield Saye, home of the Duke of Wellington. What was the name of the charger Wellington rode all day at the Battle of Waterloo?

458 Where was the Duke of Wellington's London home?

459 What was the last public position Wellington held before his death?

Junctions 12 to 13

460 Which classic children's story is set on the banks of the Thames near the author's home in Pangbourne, north of Junction 12?

461 Aldermaston lies a few miles from Junction 12. What were the Aldermaston Marches?

462 What was the Roman name for Silchester, south of the motorway between Junctions 12 and 13?

463 What, in a Roman city, was the Forum?

464 South of the motorway just before Junction 13 is a small village called Hermitage. In which city is a celebrated art collection housed in a building of the same name?

465 Junction 13 leads to Newbury. What is the name of the airbase just south of the town?

466 For which sport is Newbury well known?

467 How old must thoroughbred horses be before they can compete in flat races?

Junctions 13 to 14

468 Which two races make up the Spring Double, and which two the Autumn Double, and where are they run?

469 Which former Champion National Hunt Jockey now writes successful thrillers, many of them on racing themes?

470 For how long did Cromwell's forces besiege Donnington Castle, now south of Junction 13?

471 Which Anglo-Saxon monarch was born in Wantage, now north of Junction 14?

Junction 14 to Membury Services

472 When is Hock Tuesday?

473 The Roman mosaic at Littlecote, south of the motorway, shows Orpheus playing his lyre. What was the name of Orpheus' wife?

474 Charles II stayed at Littlecote with his queen in 1663. What was her name, and from which country did she come?

475 Which hero of which celebrated nineteenth-century novel spent his childhood in the Vale of the White Horse, north of the motorway?

Membury Services to Junction 15

476 You are about to cross the Berkshire/Wiltshire boundary. Which are the county towns of these two counties?

477 Wayland's Smithy is an ancient monument on the Wiltshire Downs south of the motorway. Who was Wayland?

478 Numerous long barrows such as Wayland's Smithy have been found on the Downs. For what purpose was a long barrow constructed?

479 Dragon Hill, near Wayland's Smithy, is said to be the spot where the dragon was slain. By whom?

480 Which ancient track crosses the motorway shortly before Junction 15?

Junctions 15 to 16

481 Marlborough lies south of Junction 15. What was the original name of the 1st Duke of Marlborough?

482 At which battle did he inflict a decisive defeat on the forces of Louis XIV of France?

483 Between these junctions the motorway runs south of Swindon. Which well-known national chain of booksellers, news-agents and stationers has its headquarters at Swindon?

484 What is the original meaning of the name Swindon?

485 Which famous Swindon-built steam locomotive, now in preservation, carries a bell to commemorate its visit, when new, to the centenary celebrations of the Baltimore & Ohio Railroad in the USA?

486 Shortly before Junction 16 the motorway crosses the main line from London to Bristol. Which engineer built the line, and when did the first through train run between Bristol and London?

Junctions 16 to 17

487 When were the standing stones at Avebury, south of the motorway, erected?

488 Malmesbury, north of Junction 17, is the oldest borough in England. When was it given its charter, and by whom?

489 Who was the first king of all England?

490 Malmesbury has close links with the USA. Who was the first President of the United States of America?

491 Which President of the USA was assassinated at Ford's Theatre, Washington, in 1865?

492 Who wrote *Leviathan*?

Junction 17 to Leigh Delamere Services

493 Who made the world's first photographic negative?

Leigh Delamere Services to Junction 18

494 Of which rock are the Cotswold Hills, north of the motorway, largely formed?

495 Between the fourteenth and seventeenth centuries the Cotswolds were one of the richest areas of England. What was the source of the area's wealth?

496 Halfway between these junctions the motorway crosses the Roman Fosse Way. How many miles of road did the Romans build in Britain?

497 Which aristocratic family lives at Great Badminton, north of the motorway?

498 The horse trials held annually at Badminton are one of the country's most important equestrian events. What is tested on each day of this three-day event?

499 What is the name of the missile used in the game of badminton?

Junctions 18 to 19

500 Junction 18 leads south to Bath. Who, in the eighteenth century, published a code of manners for visitors to Bath, and also built the first Pump Room there?

501 Who invented the most common English shorthand system?

502 What is a Bath Oliver, and who was Oliver?

503 When was the planet Uranus discovered, and by whom?

504 What is a Bath bun?

505 The motorway is now running along the northern edge of Bristol. How many football teams does the city have, what are they called, and when was the last time a Bristol team played in the Cup Final?

Junctions 19 to 20

506 Which city is further west, Bristol or Edinburgh?

507 Which well-known radical politician represented Bristol South-East from 1950 to 1983?

Junctions 20 to 21

508 Which ship, launched in Bristol in 1843, was abandoned in the Falkland Islands and finally returned to her native city in 1970?

509 The Severn Rail Tunnel starts near Severn Beach, south of the motorway. When was it opened?

Junctions 21 to 22

510 How long is the main span of the Severn Bridge, and how high are the two superstructure towers?

511 Which river, besides the Severn, does the Severn Bridge cross?

Junctions 22 to 23

512 Tintern Abbey is a few miles north of Junction 22. Who wrote the poem *Lines Composed A Few Miles Above Tintern Abbey*?

513 You have now crossed the border into Wales, and are travelling through the county of Gwent. What is the original meaning of the word Gwent?

514 What are the ingredients of Welsh cakes?

515 What is laverbread?

516 What is the Welsh name for the Welsh Nationalist Party, and how many MPs did it get elected to Westminster in the 1983 general election?

517 Who is the patron saint of Wales?

Junctions 23 to 24

518 In Magor, just by the motorway at Junction 23, are the ruins of a thirteenth-century Procurator's House. What was a Procurator?

519 The British Steel Corporation's Llanwern Works lie south of the motorway before Junction 24. Which three products are used to make steel?

Junctions 24 to 25

520 The Roman city of Caerleon lies north of the motorway between these junctions. Which Roman legion was quartered there, and of how many men did it consist?

521 The amphitheatre at Caerleon is the largest in Britain. For what were Roman amphitheatres used?

Junctions 25 to 26

522 The motorway is now running north of Newport. On which river does the town stand?

523 Which Newport-born poet wrote *The Autobiography of a Super-Tramp*?

Junctions 26 to 27

524 The valley to the north of Junction 27 forms the administrative area of Islwyn. Who is MP for Islwyn?

Junctions 27 to 28

525 Who was Islwyn?

Junctions 28 to 29

526 The grounds of Tredegar House close to Junction 28 contain a statue of Sir Briggs, a horse ridden at the Charge of the Light Brigade. In which battle did the charge take place, and who commanded the Light Brigade?

Junctions 29 to 32

527 Just beyond Junction 29, the motorway crosses the county boundary between Gwent and South Glamorgan. How many counties are there in Wales?

528 Between Junctions 29 and 33 the motorway skirts the northern edge of Cardiff. In which year did the city become the capital of Wales?

529 Which town did Owain Glyndwr proclaim as the capital of Wales in the early fifteenth century?

530 Captain Scott set sail from Cardiff in 1910 on his last expedition to the Antarctic. What were the names of his four companions?

531 Who reached the South Pole before them?

532 Who designed Castell Coch, visible immediately north of the motorway at Junction 32, and when was it built?

Junctions 32 to 33

533 What sport is played at Cardiff Arms Park?

534 When and where was the title of Prince of Wales conferred on Prince Charles?

Junctions 33 to 34

535 What is the motto of the Prince of Wales?

536 Junction 34 leads to Llantrisant, where the Royal Mint moved in 1968. Where was the Mint previously situated?

Junctions 34 to 35

537 How many £1 coins are in circulation in the United Kingdom?

538 How many circulating coins are produced each year at the Royal Mint?

539 Tonypandy is a small mining town some miles north of the motorway. By which name is Viscount Tonypandy better known?

Junctions 35 to 36

540 Between these junctions the motorway crosses from South Glamorgan into Mid-Glamorgan. What is the Welsh for Glamorgan?

541 What percentage of the population of Wales is able to speak Welsh, and what percentage can speak only Welsh?

542 What is the highest mountain in Wales, and how high is it?

Junction 36 to Sarn Park Services

543 What is the flag of Wales?

Sarn Park Services to Junction 37

544 When and where was the Prince of Wales invested?

545 Porthcawl is a coastal town just south of Junction 37. What does Porthcawl mean in English?

Junctions 37 to 38

546 Just beyond Junction 37 the motorway crosses the main South Wales railway near the Margam marshalling yard. How much freight traffic does British Rail carry each year?

547 The British Steel Corporation's Port Talbot works are clearly visible. From which countries does the iron ore used to make steel come?

Junctions 38 to 39

548 How big is the water area of the docks at Port Talbot?

Junctions 39 to 40

549 Which Port Talbot born actor played Treves in *The Elephant Man*, Captain Bligh in *The Bounty* and Lambert Leroux in the National Theatre's production of *Pravda*, among many other roles?

Junctions 40 to 41

550 The star of such successful films as *Where Eagles Dare*, *The Wild Geese*, *The Taming of the Shrew* and *The Sandpiper* was born in the village of Pontrhydyfen in the hills behind Junction 40. What was his name?

Junctions 41 to 44

551   The link between Junctions 41 and 44 is on ordinary roads. A lightship is among the exhibits at the Maritime and Industrial Museum in Swansea. Which organization is responsible for running the lighthouses and lightships around the coast of England and Wales?

552   Who wrote *Portrait of the Artist as a Young Dog* and *Under Milk Wood*?

Junctions 44 to 45

553   Which was the first railway to carry fare-paying passengers?

Junctions 45 to 46

554   Which river flows through Swansea?

Junctions 46 to 47

555   Who scored a record six sixes in a single over at a first-class cricket match held in Swansea in 1968?

Junctions 47 to 48

556   What were the Rebecca riots?

557   For what industry is Milford Haven well known?

558   Which future king of England was born at Pembroke Castle?

559   The motorway ends near Ammanford, from where you can drive on to Carmarthen and Pembrokeshire. In about 1450 one of the earliest eisteddfods was held in Carmarthen. What is the National Eisteddfod?

Junctions 48 to 49

560   What are coracles made of, and for what are they used?

561   During the 1920s Pendine Sands, south of St Clears, was used for attempts on the World Land Speed Record. What was the maximum speed achieved on the Sands, and by whom?

562   Which speed record-holder was killed on the Sands in 1927?

563   Who broke the World Land Speed Record in 1983, and what speed did he achieve?

564   What happened at Fishguard in February 1797?

M40

Junctions 1 to 1a

565 The motorway starts a short distance from Uxbridge, which is one of the termini of the Piccadilly Line. Which underground station has the longest escalator, and how long is it?

Junctions 1a to 2

566 Which celebrated seventeenth-century epic poem was written in Chalfont St Giles, now north of the motorway?

567 Who founded the state of Pennsylvania in the USA, and what does the name mean?

568 Pennsylvania was one of the original thirteen states of the USA. What were the names of the other twelve?

Junctions 2 to 3

569 The adventures of a clerical sleuth were written in Beaconsfield, close to Junction 2. What was the detective's name, and who created him?

570 Which well-known artist was born in and lived at Cookham, now south of the motorway?

Junctions 3 to 4

571 Junction 4 is the exit for High Wycombe. For what industry has the town long been famous?

572 Which novelist and Prime Minister lived at Hughenden House, north of High Wycombe?

Junctions 4 to 5

573 Who created the character of Frankenstein?

574 West Wycombe is an attractive village which has been partly owned by the National Trust for the last fifty years. Which family owned it from the late seventeenth century, and retains close connections with it today?

575 Between these junctions the motorway runs across the high lands of the Chilterns. What are the Chiltern Hundreds?

576 Of what rock are the Chilterns formed?

Junctions 5 to 6
577   What is the highest point of the Chilterns?

Junctions 6 to 7
578   The Prime Minister's country home is further east in the Chilterns. What is it called, and who presented it to the nation?
579   What tax did John Hampden, the seventeenth-century parliamentarian from Hampden in the Chilterns, refuse to pay to Charles I in 1636?
580   William Lenthall, a celebrated seventeenth-century Speaker of the House of Commons, was educated at Thame, north of the motorway. Who is the present Speaker?

Junction 7 to end of motorway
581   Many travellers on the M40 are heading for Oxford. Oxford University is the second oldest in Europe. Which is the oldest?
582   How many Oxford colleges are there?
583   What were Oxford bags?
584   What is a Blue?
585   Who were burned at the stake in Oxford in 1555?

M5

Junction 8 (M6) to Junction 1
586 Until Junction 3 the motorway runs along the western edge of Birmingham. Which character in which nineteenth-century novel remarks 'One has not great hopes from Birmingham. I always say there is something direful in the sound'?

Junctions 1 to 2
587 Junction 1 leads to West Bromwich. How often has West Bromwich Albion played in the Cup Final, and when did they win?
588 Which celebrated Pre-Raphaelite painter, who took inspiration from Greek myths and Arthurian tales, was born in Birmingham?

Junctions 2 to 3
589 In 1712 the first practical steam engine began work in Dudley, reached from Junction 2. Who invented the engine, and for what was it used?
590 What is the model village built by the Quaker chocolate manufacturers George and Richard Cadbury for their workers?
591 Which entertainer has been a director of Birmingham City Football Club?

Junction 3 to Frankley Services
592 One of the statues in the grounds of Hagley Hall, west of the motorway between Junctions 3 and 4, is of Frederick, Prince of Wales. Of which monarch was Frederick the son, and of which the father?

Frankley Services to Junction 4
593 Gladstone is among the many famous people who visited Hagley Hall. On how many occasions did Gladstone become Prime Minister, and who was his chief Tory opponent?
594 The River Stour runs some miles west of the motorway. How many other river Stours are there in England?
595 Kidderminster is an important town on the Worcestershire Stour. What is it famous for manufacturing?

Junctions 4 to 5

596 At Junction 4 the motorway passes close to British Leyland's Longbridge factory, where Minis are assembled. When was the first Mini produced?

597 Between these junctions the motorway runs west of Bromsgrove. Which old boy of Bromsgrove Grammar School failed his final exams at Oxford, but went on to become a professor at Cambridge and a celebrated poet?

598 Among the buildings re-erected at the Avoncroft Museum of Buildings, near Junction 5, are a prefab and an ice house. What is a prefab?

Junctions 5 to 6

599 What was an ice house?

600 A sequence of paintings at Hanbury Hall, east of the motorway, tells the story of Achilles. In which war was this legendary Greek hero killed, and how?

601 For which natural phenomenon has Droitwich, near Junction 5, been known since Roman times?

602 Droitwich is the birthplace of Edward Winslow, one of the Pilgrim Fathers. What was the name of the boat on which the Pilgrim Fathers sailed to America, and in which year did they leave England?

Junctions 6 to 7

603 Between these junctions, the motorway runs east of Worcester. Which monarch is buried in Worcester Cathedral?

604 Which side did Worcester take in the English Civil War?

605 Which celebrated composer succeeded his father as organist of St George's Roman Catholic Church, Worcester?

606 In which cities other than Worcester is the Three Choirs Festival held?

Junction 7 to Strensham Services

607 Which type of fruit has a variety named after Worcester?

608 The motorway is now running through the heart of Worcestershire. Who manufactures Worcestershire Sauce, and what are its ten ingredients?

609 The Vale of Evesham, where much fruit is grown, is a few miles east of the motorway. What is it in fruit that makes it set in jam?

610 Who won the Battle of Evesham in 1265, and who lost?

Strensham Services to Junction 8

611 How high is Bredon Hill, to the east of the motorway?

Junctions 8 to 9

612 Junction 9 leads to Tewkesbury, which was visited by Mr Pickwick. What was the name of Mr Pickwick's servant?

613 Who was victorious at the Battle of Tewkesbury, and of which war was it the final battle?

614 What condiment used to be made at Tewkesbury, and what did Shakespeare have to say about it?

Junctions 9 to 10

615 Which two rivers meet at Tewkesbury?

616 Which of Henry VIII's wives is buried at Sudeley Castle, now east of the motorway?

Junctions 10 to 11

617 Between Junctions 10 and 11 the motorway skirts the western edge of Cheltenham Spa. When is the Cheltenham Gold Cup run, over what distance, and what weights do the competitors carry?

618 What was the 'Cheltenham Flyer'?

619 The town of Spa, where mineral springs were discovered in the fourteenth century, has given its name to all health resorts. In which country is Spa?

620 Which Cheltenham-born composer wrote *The Planets* suite?

Junctions 11 to 12

621 Between these junctions the motorway runs along the eastern edge of Gloucester. What profession does the present Duke of Gloucester follow?

622 What is the connection between a tailor from Gloucester, a gardener called Mr McGregor, the wise Mr Brown, and Mrs Tabitha Twitchit?

623 What happened to Dr Foster when he went to Gloucester?

624 What, in the story of *The Tailor of Gloucester*, happened when the cathedral clock struck twelve on Christmas Eve?

625 Which Gloucester-born philanthropist founded the Sunday School movement?

626 The motorway is now running through Gloucestershire. Why was Double Gloucester cheese so called?

Junctions 12 to 13

627 Which celebrated cricketer played for Gloucestershire between 1865 and 1908?

628 Junction 13 leads east to Stroud, for long an important centre of the cloth industry. For what colour dye is the town world-famous?

Junctions 13 to Michael Wood Services

629 Who lives at Gatcombe Park near Stroud?

630 By the church in Frampton-on-Severn, just west of Junction 13, stands a Judas tree. How did this tree come by its name, and what is unusual about its flowering?

631 Who founded the Wildfowl Trust, whose headquarters are at Slimbridge, just west of the motorway?

632 Slimbridge is the main wintering area for White-fronted Geese. Where do they spend the summer?

633 How is it possible to tell one Bewick's Swan from another?

634 Berkeley lies west of the motorway between Junction 13 and the service station. Which English king was murdered at Berkeley Castle and buried in Gloucester Cathedral?

635 The physician Edward Jenner was born in Berkeley. For what medical discovery is he best known?

636 In which state of the USA is the city of Berkeley located?

Michael Wood Services to Junction 14

637 What is the meaning of the name Michael?

Junctions 14 to 15

638 Who lives at Highgrove, near Tetbury, west of the motorway?

639 How long is the River Severn, which runs west of the motorway, and where does it rise?

640 What is the Severn Bore?

641 Henry VIII and Anne Boleyn spent some time at Thornbury Castle, now west of the motorway. Where was Anne Boleyn executed, and for what reason?

Junctions 15 to 16

642 The *Concorde* supersonic airliner was built at the British Aircraft Corporation works at Filton, east of the motorway. Which two countries collaborated to build the aircraft, when was its first flight, and how many went into regular service?

Junctions 16 to 17

643 What was the name of *Concorde*'s Soviet rival, and when did it make its first flight?

Junctions 17 to 18

644 Between these two junctions the motorway runs along the western edge of Bristol. The explorer John Cabot set sail from the city in 1497. What was he searching for, what did he find, and what was the name of his vessel?

645 What does 'all shipshape and Bristol fashion' mean?

646 Which well-known sherry and wine importer has its head-quarters in Bristol?

Junctions 18 to 19

647 Between these junctions the motorway crosses the River Avon. Who built the Clifton Suspension Bridge a few miles upstream, and how high above the Avon is it?

Junctions 19 to 20

648 Which Bristol-born actor starred in such films as *To Catch a Thief* and *North by Northwest*?

649 The writers William Makepeace Thackeray and Alfred Lord Tennyson were frequent visitors to Clevedon Court, now near Junction 20, in the nineteenth century. Of which of Thackeray's novels is Becky Sharp the heroine?

650 In which of his poems does Tennyson write of St Andrew's Church, Clevedon?

651 Which English nurse was executed in Brussels in 1915 for helping Belgian and Allied fugitives?

Junctions 20 to 21

652 What are the names of the two islands in the Bristol Channel west of Weston-super-Mare?

653 John Cleese, the celebrated comic actor and writer, was brought up in Weston. Who are the proprietors of the Fawlty Towers Hotel?

654 Which breed was the dead parrot in the *Monty Python* sketch?

Junction 21 to Brent Knoll Rest Area

655 Who was the first person to transmit wireless signals across the Atlantic?

656 The Mendips, east of the motorway, are a well-known caving area. What is the difference between a pothole and a cave?

657 What is the difference between a stalagmite and a stalactite?

658 Of which rock are the Mendip Hills chiefly formed?

659 How high is Brent Knoll, just west of the motorway?

Brent Knoll Rest Area to Junction 22

660 The Royal Clarence Hotel in Burnham-on-Sea, west of Junction 22, was built in 1829. Who was then Duke of Clarence?

661 Wedmore lies east of the motorway at Junction 22. Between whom was the Peace of Wedmore concluded in 878?

Junctions 22 to 23

662 Glastonbury lies some miles east of Junction 23. Who, according to legend, founded the first Christian church in England at Glastonbury, and what is said to have been buried in a stream on the Tor?

663 Which mythical hero and military leader is said in legend also to be buried at Glastonbury?

Junctions 23 to 24

664 Between these junctions the motorway runs along the eastern edge of Bridgwater. Which river flows through the town?

665 Which native of Bridgwater was in command of the English fleet during the 1650s?

666 Which were the last Royalist strongholds to fall in the English Civil War?

Junctions 24 to 25

667 What is the name of the range of hills that runs from west of the motorway to the sea?

668 Which poet lived at Nether Stowey in the last years of the eighteenth century?

669 Who was defeated at the Battle of Sedgemoor, which took place at a site now west of the motorway in 1685?

670 What was the 'bloody Assize' and who presided over it?

671 The motorway is now running through Somerset. Where is Somerset House, and who now occupies it?

672 Willow-growing and basket-making are traditional Somerset activities. What name is given to the willow used in basket work?

673 Which three alcoholic drinks are made from apples?

Junction 25 to Taunton Deane Services

674 Who was Perkin Warbeck?

675 Taunton is the home of Somerset County Cricket Club. Which two players were sacked from the team at the end of the 1986 season?

Taunton Deane Services to Junction 26

676 What are the hills south of the motorway called?

Junctions 26 to 27

677 How tall is the Wellington Monument above the motorway?

678 Where was Napoleon exiled after being defeated by Wellington at the Battle of Waterloo?

679 Halfway between these junctions the motorway crosses into Devon. Where is the seat of the Dukes of Devonshire?

680 Who wrote, in which poem, that 'Drake he was a Devon man, an' ruled the Devon seas'?

681 Tiverton lies a few miles west of Junction 27. Which well-known march is claimed to have been first played for a wedding on the organ of St Peter's Church in the town?

Junctions 27 to 28

682 Which former pupil of Blundell's School, Tiverton, wrote the celebrated West Country novel *Lorna Doone*?

683 East of Junction 27 is Coldharbour Mill, a working wool museum. What is a leat?

684 What is worsted, and where does the name originate?

Junctions 28 to 29

685 The motorway is now running alongside a river and a railway. What is the name of the river?

686 The railway was formerly run by the Great Western Railway (GWR). To what gauge was the line originally built?

687 What were the initials GWR said to stand for by the company's supporters; and by its detractors?

688 How many passenger stations are there on the British Rail network in Great Britain?

689 Who was in command of the *Mary Rose* when she sank in the Solent?

690 Who wrote *The History of Pendennis*, which is set in Ottery St Mary, now east of Junction 29?

Junctions 29 to 30

691   Between Junctions 29 and 31 the motorway runs south of Exeter. What was the purpose of the underground passages built in Exeter during the Middle Ages?

692   What is the motto of the city of Exeter?

Junctions 30 to 31

693   Which radical Archbishop of Canterbury was born in Exeter?

694   One of Exeter's attractions is a Maritime Museum. What is a dhow, and where would you expect to see one?

695   Who was captain of the *Bounty* and what happened to him near the Friendly Islands?

M50

Junction 8 (M5) to Junction 1
696 The composer Edward Elgar lived for years in Malvern, north of the motorway. Which of his works takes the form of a musical portrait of fourteen of his friends?

Junctions 1 to 2
697 How many concertos did Elgar write, and for which instruments?

698 Why did Dr John Wall become famous in 1756?

699 What is the highest point of the Malvern Hills?

700 The motorway is now running through Herefordshire. Hops are a local crop. What drink are they used to make, and what is the name of the building in which they are dried?

701 The poet John Masefield was born in Ledbury, north of Junction 2. What was the cargo on board his 'dirty British coaster', and where and when was she sailing?

702 Masefield was Poet Laureate from 1930 to 1967. Who succeeded him?

703 Another poet, Elizabeth Barret Browning, spent much of her childhood near Ledbury. Where was her London home?

Junctions 2 to 3
704 The Falconry Centre at Newent is a short distance from Junction 3. Where were birds of prey kept in the Middle Ages?

705 What breed of dog is used in game-hawking?

706 What is the maximum speed at which a falcon can fly?

Junctions 3 to 4
707 Hellens, a country mansion north of Junction 3, contains a stone table at which the Black Prince once dined. Why is he so called?

708 Junction 4 leads into Ross-on-Wye. How long is the River Wye, and where does it rise?

709 On whose life did Terence Rattigan base his play *Ross*?

710 What is Hay-on-Wye, further up the Wye, famous for selling?

M54

Junction 10a (M6) to Junction 1
711   Which king took refuge from his pursuers at Moseley Old Hall, now beside the motorway?

Junctions 1 to 2
712   The M54 carries traffic to the new town of Telford and on to Shrewsbury and North Wales. Which rebellious prince was killed at the Battle of Shrewsbury in 1403?

Junctions 2 to 3
713   Charles Darwin was a native of Shrewsbury. What was the name of the ship on which he explored South America in the 1830s?
714   What is Offa's Dyke?
715   Bridgnorth, south-west of the motorway, is one terminus of the Severn Valley Railway, a preserved steam line. Which was the first standard-gauge line in England to be opened as a privately-operated steam railway?
716   Which is the oldest of the narrow-gauge Welsh steam lines still operating?
717   The Aerospace Museum at Cosford is just to the south of Junction 3. On display is one of the early British jet engines. Who designed the first jet engine intended specifically for aircraft propulsion, and when did it first run?

Junctions 3 to 4
718   Which was the first British aircraft powered by a turbojet, and when did it fly for the first time?
719   Who was the first man to travel in space?
720   Telford new town, reached from Junctions 4, 5 and 6, is named after the Scottish engineer Thomas Telford. One of his projects was the Caledonian Canal in Scotland. Which towns stand near each end of the Canal?

Junctions 4 to 5
721   Which London docks did Telford build?

Junctions 5 to 6
722 For what product is Coalport, south of the motorway, famous?

Junctions 6 to 7
723 The world's first iron bridge was built in 1778 at Ironbridge, south of the motorway. Who designed it?

724 The motorway ends north of the distinctive hill called The Wrekin. How tall is it?

M55

Junction 32 (M6) to Junction 1
725 The M55 carries holiday-makers to Blackpool, and commercial traffic to the docks at Fleetwood. How tall is Blackpool Tower?

Junctions 1 to 3
726 How many light bulbs and miles of wiring and cable are used in the celebrated Blackpool Illuminations?

727 How many foreigners visited Britain on holiday in 1985?

728 Which country sent most visitors in 1985?

729 For what sport is Lytham St Anne's, south of the motorway, famous?

730 Who or what is Ernie?

Junctions 3 to 4
731 On the mouth of which river does Fleetwood stand?

732 Which footballer was nicknamed the 'Blackpool Bomber'?

733 Who became player-manager of Blackpool in 1980 but was sacked the following year?

M6

Junction 19 (M1) to Junction 1
734 The motorway starts north-east of Rugby, where Rugby Football originated. How many players make up a Rugby Union team, and how many a Rugby League team?
735 What in Rugby Union must a side do to win the Grand Slam?

Junctions 1 to 2
736 Which revered nineteenth-century headmaster regenerated Rugby School?
737 Between Junctions 1 and 2 the motorway crosses the Roman Fosse Way. Which cities did this route link?
738 What is an 'agger'?
739 Coombe Abbey, near Junction 2, is a country park centred around a ruined abbey. What is the name given to the dress worn by monks and nuns?

Junctions 2 to 3
740 Between Junction 2 and Corley Services the motorway runs along the northern edge of Coventry. Who rode naked through the streets of the city in the eleventh century, and why?
741 What happens if someone is 'sent to Coventry'?
742 Which architect designed the modern Coventry cathedral, and which artist was responsible for the altar tapestry?

Junction 3 to Corley Services
743 What was a penny farthing?
744 What was the first car bought by a member of the royal family?

Corley Services to Junction 4
745 Under what pseudonym did Mary Ann Evans publish her novels?
746 The churchyard at Meriden, south of the motorway, contains the tomb of the longest-surviving British officer of the Peninsular War. Who commanded the British forces during this war, and against which country was it fought?

747   Junction 4 is the junction with the M42, which leads to the National Exhibition Centre, the largest exhibition area in the country. How many miles of steel tubing are there in the roof, and how many double-decker buses could fit into the exhibition halls?

748   What celebrated event is held in October of every even-numbered year at the National Exhibition Centre?

Junctions 4 to 4a

749   Between Junctions 4 and 8 the motorway runs through Birmingham. What is the population of the city?

750   Which Lord Mayor of Birmingham went on to become Prime Minister of Great Britain?

Junctions 4a to 5

751   How many miles of canal make up the canal system in Birmingham, known as the Birmingham Canal Navigations?

Junctions 5 to 6

752   What is the name of the BBC's television and radio studio in Birmingham?

753   Junction 6 is nicknamed 'Spaghetti Junction'. What is the difference between spaghetti alla bolognese and spaghetti napolitana?

Junctions 6 to 7

754   If you were served lasagne verde, what colour would you expect the pasta to be?

755   How many professional football clubs are there in Birmingham, and what are their names?

756   Which two of Britain's 'big four' clearing banks were founded in Birmingham?

Junctions 7 to 8

757   The phenomenally successful 'Baby' Austin Seven was launched at Austin's Birmingham works in 1922. For what price was it originally sold?

Junctions 8 to 9

758   At Junction 9 the motorway is running between Walsall and Wednesbury. Which Walsall-born author wrote *Three Men In A Boat*?

759   What is the nickname of Walsall's football team?

Junctions 9 to 10
760   After whom was Wednesbury named?

Junctions 10 to 10a
761   Junction 10 leads west to Willenhall and Wolverhampton. What industry is centred on Willenhall?
762   Which Wolverhampton Wanderers player captained England 90 times, and how many caps did he win?
763   Who was one of Wolverhampton's MPs from 1950 to 1974?

Junction 10a to Hilton Park Services
764   Which railway engineer built the Grand Junction Railway from Birmingham to Lancashire, which runs a few miles west of the motorway?

Hilton Park Services to Junction 11
765   The labourers who built the first railways were known as navvies. What is the origin of this word?

Junctions 11 to 12
766   Jennie Lee was once MP for Cannock, north-east of Junction 11. To which well-known politician was she married?
767   Junction 12 is the junction with the Roman Watling Street. Which Roman Emperor conquered Britain, and when and where did his troops land?

Junctions 12 to 13
768   Cannock Chase lies a few miles east of the motorway between Junctions 12 and 13. What was a Chase in the Middle Ages?
769   There are several military cemeteries on Cannock Chase. Which organization is responsible for maintaining the graves of members of Commonwealth forces who fell in both world wars, and how many such burial grounds are there throughout the world?
770   What event does the Katyn Memorial on Cannock Chase commemorate?
771   The motorway is now in the heart of Staffordshire. The Staffordshire Bull Terrier is a variety of Bull Terrier. What is the standard weight of a Bull Terrier?

Junctions 13 to 14

772 Between Junctions 13 and 14 the motorway runs west of Stafford, where Izaak Walton was born. Which is his best-known book today, and for what type of writing was he most famous during his lifetime?

773 The remains of Stafford Castle can be seen to the right. What is the word used to describe the demolition of a castle after it has been captured by enemy forces?

774 The playwright Richard Brinsley Sheridan was MP for Stafford in the late eighteenth century. Which of his characters, in which of his plays, utters the following remark: 'We will not anticipate the past, so mind, young people – our retrospection will be all to the future'?

Junctions 14 to 15

775 The town of Stone, east of the motorway between these junctions, is the birthplace of Admiral Sir John Jervis, who won a famous victory off Cape St Vincent. Where is Cape St Vincent?

776 Which poet wrote the line 'Nobly, nobly Cape St Vincent to the North-west died away'?

777 Which classical writer reputedly coined the proverb 'A rolling stone gathers no moss'?

778 Who were the original members of the Rolling Stones?

779 Trentham Hall, now south of Junction 15, was designed by the Victorian architect Sir Charles Barry. For which well-known London building was he also responsible?

780 The Wedgwood factory was moved to Barlaston, east of the motorway, in 1939. In which part of Stoke-on-Trent was it previously situated?

781 Stoke-on-Trent, north-west of the motorway after Junction 15, is the capital of the English potteries. What is the name of the oven in which pots are baked?

782 What does a potter do when he 'throws' a pot?

Junction 15 to Keele Services

783 The designer of the legendary RAF *Spitfire* was born in Stoke-on-Trent in 1895. Who was he?

784 When was the University of Keele founded?

Keele Services to Junction 16

785 Six towns were amalgamated to make up the city of Stoke-on-Trent in 1910. What were their names?

786 Which novelist set many of his books in the six Pottery towns?

787 The motorway enters Cheshire shortly before Junction 16. In which story does the Cheshire Cat appear, and what was the last thing left of it?

Junction 16 to Sandbach Services

788 Crewe, north of the motorway between Junctions 16 and 17, is a well-known railway junction. How many people change trains there each year, and how many passenger and freight trains pass through each weekday?

789 In the words of the song, where did the lady who got sent to Crewe by mistake originally want to go, where had she come from, and to whom was she complaining?

790 Rolls-Royce cars are built at Crewe. What name was given to the first Rolls-Royce made?

791 Which religious movement was founded at an open-air meeting held on Mow Cop, the limestone ridge east of the motorway, in 1807?

Sandbach Services to Junction 17

792 Little Moreton Hall, near Mow Cop, has a fine Elizabethan Long Gallery. For what was a Long Gallery used?

Junctions 17 to 18

793 Which medieval sport is said to have flourished longer in Congleton, east of Junction 17, than anywhere else in Britain?

794 No less than four waterways pass through Middlewich, just west of Junction 18. What are their names?

Junction 18 to Knutsford Services

795 What is the diameter of the larger, Mark IA, telescope at the Radio Astronomy Laboratories at Jodrell Bank, near Junction 18?

796 Among the research done by radio astronomers at Jodrell Bank is work on pulsars. What are pulsars?

797 Which mineral is mined at Northwich, west of the motorway between these junctions?

798 What did the Anderton Lift, a massive piece of Victorian engineering 1 mile from Northwich, carry?

799 Which two industrialists founded an alkali works at Winnington, near Northwich, in 1873, and into which international company did it develop?

800 The novelist Mrs Gaskell lived for most of her childhood at Knutsford. What name did she give the town in one of her most popular novels?

Knutsford Services to Junction 19

801 In which of Mrs Gaskell's novels does Tatton Hall, now a short way from Junction 19, appear as the big house, and what is it called?

Junctions 19 to 20

802 Tatton Park was completely rebuilt by the Wyatt family of architects in the late eighteenth and early nineteenth centuries. How many architects did the family produce, and what were their names?

803 At Great Budworth, west of the motorway, there is some excellent pargetting. What is pargetting?

804 C.L. Dodgson, better known as the writer Lewis Carroll, was born at Daresbury, now west of Junction 20. For whom were his *Alice* stories written?

Junctions 20 to 21

805 Who attended the Mad Hatter's Tea Party?

806 The motorway crosses the Manchester Ship Canal and the river Mersey between these junctions. When was the Ship Canal opened, and how long is it?

807 Which two rivers join to form the Mersey?

Junctions 21 to 21a

808 Which group had a hit with the song *Ferry Across the Mersey* in the 1960s?

Junctions 21a to 22

809 The motorway is now running through the northern tip of Cheshire. What is the population of the county?

Junctions 22 to 23

810 Who was killed in an accident on the opening day of the Liverpool & Manchester Railway in 1830, near where the motorway now crosses the line?

811 St Helens, west of the motorway between these junctions, is the headquarters of Pilkington Glass. What materials are used to make glass?

Junctions 23 to 24
812 Haydock Park racecourse is close to Junction 23. When does the flat racing season begin and end each year?

Junctions 24 to 25
813 Which banjo- and ukulele-playing music-hall artist was born in Wigan?

Junctions 25 to 26
814 Near Junction 26 the motorway skirts Wigan to the west. What was Wigan Pier?
815 Who wrote *The Road to Wigan Pier*?

Junctions 26 to 27
816 Which well-known player started his football career playing for Skelmersdale, west of Junction 26?
817 The motorway crosses the Leeds & Liverpool Canal between Junctions 26 and 27. What is the difference between a flight and a staircase of locks?
818 The church in Standish, west of the motorway at Junction 27, is dedicated to St Wilfred, a seventh-century Bishop of York. Where was the most important centre of Christian learning in England in Anglo-Saxon times?

Junctions 27 to Charnock Richard Services
819 The village of Crofton lies a few miles west of the motorway. What does the name Crofton mean?
820 What is the meaning of the name Richard?

Charnock Richard Services to Junction 28
821 The motorway crosses the main line from London to Glasgow just south of Junction 28. What are the names of the two terminal stations of this line?
822 In which year was the first Anglo-Scottish rail link opened, and when was electrification of the line completed?
823 Leyland, just west of Junction 28, was the original headquarters of what is now British Leyland. What did the Leyland group originally manufacture?

Junctions 28 to 29
824 Who, in the late 1970s and early 1980s, rescued British Leyland from virtual bankruptcy?

Junctions 29 to 30

825 At Junction 30 the motorway meets the M61 which runs south to Chorley. Which sugar magnate, who also founded a well-known art gallery, was born here in 1819?

Junctions 30 to 31

826 Between Junctions 30 and 32 the motorway runs along the eastern edge of Preston. On which river does the town stand?

Junctions 31 to 32

827 Preston-born Sir Richard Arkwright invented the frame. Was this machine used for spinning or weaving?

828 What happened at the Battle of Preston in 1648?

829 Which former Preston North End player went on to manage the club from 1977 to 1981?

830 Which Preston-born poet had these words inscribed on his tombstone: 'Look for me in the nurseries of Heaven'?

Junction 32 to Forton Services

831 What are Goosnargh cakes, from the tiny village of Goosnargh, just east of Junction 32?

832 The little village of Inglewhite, east of the motorway at the foot of Beacon Fell, has two village greens, one a 'goose' green. What was a goose green used for?

833 Further east, at Chipping, a regular Candlemas Fair was held. When is Candlemas Day, and what does it commemorate?

834 Fleetwood, some miles west of the motorway, is an important port for the Isle of Man. How many people live on the island, and where is its capital?

835 What is the name of the parliament of the Isle of Man, and which part of it is elected?

836 Which well-known sporting event takes place each year on the Isle of Man?

Forton Services to Junction 33

837 What is the special characteristic of Manx cats?

838 At Thurnham Hall, west of Junction 33, a replica of the Shroud of Turin used to be exhibited. What is the Shroud?

839 Which river reaches the sea at Glasson Dock, a few miles to the west?

Junctions 33 to 34

840   Between these junctions the motorway runs along the eastern edge of Lancaster. Who is the present Duke of Lancaster?

841   Which famous cabinet-making firm, still commemorated in the name of a major furniture retailing chain, originated in Lancaster?

842   Lancaster was an early Quaker centre. What is the proper name for the Quaker movement?

Junctions 34 to 35

843   Which well-known 1940s romantic film was partly shot on Carnforth station?

844   Which was the last standard-gauge steam locomotive regularly used by British Rail?

Junction 35 to Burton Services

845   Bitterns regularly breed at Leighton Moss Bird Reserve west of Carnforth. What colour is a bittern's plumage, and what does its call sound like?

846   Ospreys are occasional visitors to Leighton Moss. Where do these birds spend the winter?

Burton Services to Junction 36

847   St Michael's Church at Beetham, west of the motorway, is approached under a pergola of rambler roses. What is a pergola?

848   A short way from Junction 36 is Levens Hall, where there is a magnificent topiary garden. What is topiary?

849   One of the forebears of the present owner of Levens Hall established the Rush-Bagot Treaty of 1817. Which conflict did this treaty resolve?

850   Junctions 36 and 37 both lead west to Kendal. Which of Henry VIII's six wives was born in the town?

Junction 36 to Killington Lake Services

851   Which two world-famous products are manufactured in Kendal? (You wear one and eat the other.)

852   What was Kendal Green?

853   Until Junction 40 the motorway runs along the eastern edge of the Lake District. Which well-known writer on the Lake District was formerly treasurer of Kendal Borough Council?

854   Which are the three highest peaks in the Lake District, and how high are they?

Killington Lake Services to Junction 37

855 By what name was Beatrix Potter better known when she lived at Sawrey, near Hawkshead?

Junctions 37 to 38

856 What was Mrs Tiggy-Winkle's profession?

857 In *The Tale of Peter Rabbit*, which items of clothing did Peter Rabbit lose, and where did he lose them?

858 Of which national organization was Beatrix Potter an early benefactor?

859 Which is the largest Lake District lake?

860 Which celebrated nineteenth-century writer and critic lived at the edge of Coniston Water?

861 What was the name of the cottage in which the poet William Wordsworth lived at Grasmere?

862 From which of Wordsworth's poems do the following lines come, and to what do they refer?
'Bliss was it in that dawn to be alive,
But to be young was very heaven!'

Junction 38 to Tebay (West) Services

863 What are the names of the two Langdale Pikes?

Tebay (West) Services to Junction 39

864 Which is the highest Lake District pass accessible by road?

865 To which city do Haweswater and Thirlmere supply water?

Junctions 39 to 40

866 Who wrote the Swallows and Amazons stories?

867 What are the names of the Swallows and the Amazons and on which island did they first meet?

868 What name did the Swallows and Amazons give to Coniston Old Man when they climbed it in *Swallowdale*?

869 Which village is generally held to be Britain's wettest inhabited place, and what is its average annual rainfall?

870 What is the name of the Lake District breed of sheep?

871 Which sequence of novels did Hugh Walpole set in the countryside around Borrowdale and Keswick?

Junctions 40 to 41

872 Which poet and resident of Keswick was appointed Poet Laureate in 1813?

873 Which celebrated huntsman is buried in Caldbeck church-yard, reached from Junction 40, and what colour was his coat?

Junction 41 to Southwaite Services

874 Which mountaineer is famous for his Himalayan expeditions and for being one of the first British climbers to conquer the North Face of the Eiger?
875 This part of the motorway is in the former county of Cumberland. Who was 'Butcher' Cumberland?
876 How are Cumberland hams traditionally matured?
877 What are the rules of Cumberland wrestling?

Southwaite Services to Junction 42

878 East of the motorway after Junction 41 are two railway lines. The more easterly is the famous Settle to Carlisle route. Which railway company built this route, and why?
879 Which is the highest station in England?

Junctions 42 to 43

880 These two junctions lead into Carlisle. Which three rivers meet in the town?
881 Downing Street was built by Sir George Downing, who was once MP for Carlisle. Who live at numbers 10 and 11 Downing Street, and whose office is at number 12?
882 What was the Roman name for Carlisle?
883 Before 1923, no less than seven railway companies ran into Carlisle Citadel station. Which were they?

Junctions 43 to 44

884 Between these junctions the motorway crosses the line of Hadrian's Wall. How long is the Wall, what are its two end points, and why was it built?
885 Which English monarch died at Burgh-on-Sands near Carlisle, west of the motorway at Junction 44?
886 The A7 and the A74 take traffic north across the border. Who wrote, in which play, 'God help England if she had no Scots to think for her'?

M62

Junctions 4 to 5

887 The motorway starts at Junction 4, about 4 miles from the centre of Liverpool. In which Liverpool night club were the Beatles discovered, and who were the original members of the group?

888 Who was manager of Liverpool when they won the FA Cup in 1965 and 1974?

Junctions 5 to 6

889 Junction 5 leads to Huyton and Knotty Ash. Who was MP for Huyton until 1983?

890 Why is Knotty Ash so called, and which comedian made the place famous?

Junctions 6 to 7

891 Edward Lear stayed at Knowsley Hall, now near Junction 6, in the 1830s, and wrote many of his nonsense verses there. Who 'went to sea in a beautiful pea-green boat', what did they take with them, and to where did they sail?

892 The grounds of Knowsley Hall now contain a safari park with, among other inhabitants, a fine collection of African Elephants. What is the maximum height and weight African Elephants attain, and what is their gestation period?

Junction 7 to Burtonwood Services

893 Junction 7 leads off to Rainhill, where in 1829 the Rainhill Trials were held to select a locomotive for the Liverpool & Manchester Railway. Which loco was chosen, and who built it?

894 What were the original terminal stations of the Liverpool & Manchester Railway?

895 G. and J. Greenall manufacture gin and vodka at their Warrington distilleries. Which ingredients are used to make gin?

Burtonwood Services to Junction 9

896 How many litres of Vladivar vodka are manufactured each year in Warrington?

Junctions 9 to 10
897 Of which country is vodka the national drink, and from which crop is it distilled?

Junctions 10 to 11
898 Risley Moss, a Country Park a short distance south of Junction 11, is all that remains of the peat bogs that once covered much of the Mersey Valley. What is peat?

Junctions 11 to 12
899 Which garden plants thrive best on peat?

900 Part of Risley Moss was once a Royal Ordnance Factory. What does an ordnance factory manufacture?

901 The motorway is now running through the area formerly administered by the Greater Manchester Metropolitan Council, abolished in 1986. Which were the other five Metropolitan Councils?

902 Near Junction 12 the motorway runs near Eccles. What are the ingredients of Eccles cakes?

903 Junction 12 is near the Barton Swing Aqueduct. What is an aqueduct, and what is the derivation of the word?

Junctions 12 to 13
904 Worsley, just south of Junction 13, was the home of the 3rd Duke of Bridgewater, who gave his name to the Bridgewater canal, the first canal in Britain. Who built the canal?

Junctions 13 to 14
905 The motorway is now running along the northern edge of Manchester. Who played for Manchester City before World War Two and managed Manchester United after it?

Junctions 14 to 15
906 Which celebrated editor of the *Manchester Guardian* stated that 'Comment is free but facts are sacred'?

Junctions 15 to 17
907 Which symphony orchestra has its home in Manchester?

Junctions 17 to 18
908 Which footballer holds the record British transfer fee?

Junction 18 to Birch Services
909 Who was manager of Manchester City when they won the FA Cup in 1969; which side lost the match, and what was the score?

Birch Services to Junction 19
910 What are wakes weeks?

Junctions 19 to 20
911 Junction 20 leads south to Oldham and north to Rochdale. Which famous impersonator once had a soccer trial as a winger with Oldham?

912 Who started his political career as Conservative candidate for Oldham in 1899?

Junctions 20 to 21
913 Which Rochdale-born singer used to sing about the 'biggest aspidistra in the world'?

914 Which well-known retailing chain has its origin in a shop opened in Rochdale in 1844?

Junctions 21 to 22
915 Between Junctions 21 and 22, the motorway crosses the former Lancashire/Yorkshire boundary. In which war did the House of Lancaster and the House of York clash, and what were their respective symbols?

916 You are now driving across the Pennine Mountains. The Pennine Way long-distance footpath crosses the motorway west of Junction 22. How long is the path, and between which points does it run?

917 Which is the longest long-distance footpath in Britain?

Junctions 22 to 23
918 Which is the highest point in the Pennine chain?

919 This part of the motorway is often blocked by heavy snow. What is the greatest snowfall ever recorded in the United Kingdom?

920 For what is 'Harry Ramsden's' famous?

921 In weaving, what is the warp and what is the weft?

Junctions 23 to 24
922 Halifax and Huddersfield are the main towns served by

Junctions 23 and 24. One of the most interesting sights in Halifax is the restored Piece Hall. Why is it so called?

923 How many savings accounts are held with the Halifax Building Society, and what is the total investment?

Junctions 24 to 25

924 The Huddersfield Choral Society is world famous, especially for its performances of the *Messiah*. Who composed the work and where was it first performed?

925 For which four female and male voices is most choral music written?

926 What sport came into being at Huddersfield in August 1895?

Junction 25 to Hartshead Moor Services

927 Brighouse and Rastrick, reached from Junction 25, are famous for their brass band. Which seven instruments are found in a brass band?

Hartshead Moor Services to Junction 26

928 Junction 26 leads into Bradford. Which notable twentieth-century novelist, playwright and broadcaster was born in the city?

Junctions 26 to 27

929 One of the best-known British painters of the last 20 years, who dyes his hair blond, and painted young men underwater in swimming pools, comes from Bradford. What is his name?

930 Charlotte Brontë set part of her novel *Shirley* around Gomersal and Birstall, now south of the motorway between Junctions 26 and 27. Which three other novels did she write, and what were the names of the other Brontë sisters?

931 Which Presbyterian minister and chemist discovered oxygen?

932 Junction 27 is the link with the M621 which runs into central Leeds. What was the original name of Leeds United Football Club?

Junctions 27 to 28

933 How often have Leeds United appeared in the Cup Final; in which years have they won, and what was the score?

934 What is the daily circulation of the *Yorkshire Post*, published in Leeds?

Junctions 28 to 29

935 Under which Prime Minister were old-age pensions first paid?

936 The motorway is now running through Yorkshire. How many wickets did Wilfred Rhodes take in his 32-year career playing with Yorkshire?

Junctions 29 to 30

937 What are the ingredients of Yorkshire pudding?

Junctions 30 to 31

938 At what part of the meal is Yorkshire pudding traditionally eaten in Yorkshire?

939 Which two rivers meet at Castleford, north of Junction 31?

Junctions 31 to 32

940 Which Castleford-born sculptor has specialized in producing statues of reclining figures?

941 Featherstone lies south of the motorway between these two junctions. What sport do Featherstone Rovers play?

Junctions 32 to 33

942 Junction 32 leads south to Pontefract. Which king died a prisoner in Pontefract Castle?

943 By what name is Pontefract known in Shakespeare's plays?

944 What plant used for making sweets was Pontefract once famous for growing?

Junctions 33 to 34

945 Fairburn Ings Bird Sanctuary, north of Junction 33, attracts a wide variety of wildfowl. What are the three species of swan regularly seen in Great Britain?

946 Arctic Terns are also regular visitors. Over roughly what distance do they migrate each year?

Junctions 34 to 35

947 The Selby Coalfield lies north of Junction 34. What size is it, and how many tonnes of coal does it contain?

948 The motorway crosses the London to Edinburgh railway east of Junction 34. Which locomotive set the world speed record for steam further south on this line in 1938, and what speed was reached?

949 What are the names of the London and Edinburgh termini of this line?

950 Drax, the largest coal-fired power station in Europe, lies north of Junction 25. How many tonnes of coal does it burn every day, and what is its total output?

Junctions 35 to 36

951 What is the name given to the coal trains that supply power stations such as Drax with fuel?

952 The Aire and Calder Navigation, an important commercial canal, runs south of the motorway at Junction 35. For what sorts of cargo is canal transport most economical?

Junctions 36 to 37

953 Goole is an important port south of the motorway between these junctions. How many vessels dock in the port each year?

954 Howden Minster is visible just north of the motorway at Junction 37. What is a minster?

Junctions 37 to 38

955 Which two rivers join to form the Humber south of the motorway beyond Junction 37?

956 How long is the main span of the Humber Bridge?

957 What is the name of the spit of land that juts out into the Humber estuary where it meets the sea?

958 The motorway terminates a few miles west of Hull. Which famous poet was also a jazz critic and librarian of Hull University?

959 Which Hull-born poet wrote the following lines:
'But at my back I always hear
 Time's winged chariot hurrying near;
 And yonder all before us lie
 Deserts of vast eternity'?

960 Who led the campaign to abolish first the slave trade and then slavery itself?

961 Beverley is an attractive market town not far from the end of the motorway. Which nineteenth-century novelist was once an unsuccessful parliamentary candidate for Beverley?

M8

Junctions 1 to 2
962 The motorway starts a few miles west of Edinburgh, just beyond Edinburgh Airport. How many passengers use the airport each year, and to how many different destinations do regular scheduled services run?

Junctions 2 to 3
963 What is the Queen's official residence in Edinburgh?
964 What is Arthur's Seat?
965 Which native of Edinburgh invented the telephone?
966 What is Edinburgh's main shopping thoroughfare called?

Junctions 3 to 4
967 Between which two famous buildings in Edinburgh does the Royal Mile run?
968 What is the name of the range of hills to the south of the motorway?
969 Bathgate lies north of the motorway between these junctions. Who established the first commercial oil-works in the world here in 1851?
970 Which native of Bathgate pioneered the use of chloroform as an anaesthetic?

Junction 4 to Harthill Services
971 The motorway is now running through the Lothian region. What was the Midlothian Campaign?
972 Into how many administrative regions is Scotland divided?
973 Who is the patron saint of Scotland?

Harthill Services to Junction 5
974 When, and by which Act of Parliament, were England and Scotland united?

Junctions 5 to 6
975 How many people speak Scots Gaelic?
976 How many Scottish Nationalist MPs were elected at the 1983 general election?

977   What and where is Scotland Yard, and why is it so called?

Junctions 6 to 8
978   How many Scottish Prime Ministers have there been this century, and what are their names?

979   Airdrie lies to the north of the road. When was the last occasion Airdrieonians appeared in the Scottish Cup Final, and what was the score?

980   The road is now running through the industrial Clyde valley. How long is the river Clyde, and where does it rise?

Junctions 8 to 9
981   From Junctions 8 to 25 the motorway bisects the city of Glasgow. What is the population of Glasgow?

Junctions 9 to 10
982   Which city is further west: Glasgow or Exeter?

Junctions 10 to 11
983   Celtic and Rangers are Glasgow's two football teams. What are their respective colours?

Junctions 11 to 12
984   How many times have Celtic and Rangers each won the Scottish F.A. Cup Final since 1947?

Junctions 12 to 13
985   When was the last time Rangers and Celtic met in the Scottish Cup Final, and what was the score?

Junctions 13 to 15
986   Who made the song *I Belong to Glasgow* famous?

Junctions 15 to 17
987   The fine collection of paintings in the Glasgow Art Gallery contains works by Rembrandt, among many others. In which city did Rembrandt work?

Junctions 17 to 20
988   To which saint is Glasgow Cathedral dedicated?

989   Which Glasgow architect (one of the artist-craftsmen of the 'Glasgow School') designed the Glasgow School of Art?

Junctions 20 to 22
990 The Victorian architect Sir George Gilbert Scott was responsible for building Glasgow University. Which well-known London buildings did he design?

Junctions 22 to 24
991 Who introduced the antiseptic system?

Junctions 24 to 25
992 When did the Glasgow subway system open, and how many stations does it serve?

Junctions 25 to 26
993 Which other cities in Great Britain have subway systems?

Junctions 26 to 27
994 These two junctions lead south into Paisley and north to Renfrew. What were Paisley shawls?

Junctions 27 to 28
995 Who is the present Baron Renfrew?

Junctions 28 to 29
996 Now aircraft taking off from and landing at Glasgow Airport can be seen. How many hours of bright sunshine are there on average each year at the airport, and which is the sunniest month?

Junctions 29 to 30
997 What are the hottest and coldest temperatures recorded at the airport since record-keeping began in 1920?
998 Junction 30 leads to the Erskine Bridge over the Clyde. When was the bridge opened?

Junctions 30 to 31
999 The motorway ends on the banks of the Clyde, with Dumbarton Castle on the opposite bank. Who sailed for France from the castle in 1548?
1000 What is the original meaning of the name Dumbarton?

M9

Junctions 1 to 2

1001 The motorway starts a short distance from Queensferry and the Firth of Forth. Which English queen of a Scottish monarch gave the inhabitants of Queensferry the exclusive right to ferry her across the Forth?

1002 How long is the Firth of Forth, and by how many bridges is it crossed?

1003 A flock of rare St Kilda sheep grazes in the grounds of Hopetoun House just west of Queensferry. What colour are St Kilda sheep and how many horns do they have?

Junctions 2 to 3

1004 The Binns, just north of Junction 2, is the home of the Dalyell family. What regiment did General Tam Dalyell raise at his home in 1681?

1005 What post does the present Tam Dalyell hold?

Junctions 3 to 4

1006 Between these junctions there is a fine view of Linlithgow Palace. Which monarch started to construct the Palace?

1007 Two monarchs were born in the Palace. Who were they?

1008 What was the original name of Bo'ness, north of the motorway?

Junctions 4 to 5

1009 What was the name of the first practical steamship?

Junctions 5 to 6

1010 These junctions lead into Falkirk. What was the Antonine Wall?

Junctions 6 to 7

1011 Who was known as the 'Hammer of the Scots'?

Junctions 7 to 8

1012 Who was the first British explorer to reach the source of the Blue Nile?

Junctions 8 to 9

1013 You leave the motorway at Junction 9 for the Bannockburn Visitor Centre and the site of the battlefield. On what dates was the battle fought, and who led the Scottish and English forces?

1014 How many men fought on each side?

Junctions 9 to 10

1015 Between these junctions the motorway runs west of Stirling, with the castle dominating the town. Which monarchs were crowned in the castle?

1016 Which regiment has its headquarters in Stirling Castle?

1017 The University of Stirling, opened in 1967, was the last of the new universities created during the 1960s. Which were the other seven?

Junctions 10 to 11

1018 Doune Castle, north-west of Junction 11, was a Jacobite stronghold during the '45 uprising against English rule. Who became famous for helping Bonnie Prince Charlie to escape from Benbecula to Portree in 1746?

1019 From Dunblane, roads lead north into the Highlands. What are the Munros?

1020 Which is the highest mountain in Scotland, and how high is it?

M90

Junctions 1 to 2

1021 The motorway starts on the north bank of the Firth of Forth. How many tons of steel and cubic feet of concrete were used in the construction of the Forth Road Bridge?

Junctions 2 to 3

1022 Between these junctions the motorway runs east of Dunfermline. Which Scottish monarch and military hero is buried in the Abbey?

1023 Which native of Dunfermline emigrated to the USA and became a multi-millionnaire and worldwide benefactor?

1024 Who killed Macbeth, King of Scotland?

Junctions 3 to 4

1025 Just beyond Junction 3, the motorway crosses the railway. How many new stations were opened in Scotland in 1985 and 1986, and how many were closed?

1026 Dollar is a small town reached from Junction 4. When did the dollar become the currency of the USA, and what is the origin of the $ sign?

Junctions 4 to 5

1027 Between these junctions the motorway runs alongside Blairadam Forest, which is run by the Forestry Commission. How much productive woodland is there in Scotland, and what percentage of this consists of coniferous trees?

1028 William Adam, an architect from the Blairadam district, had four sons, all celebrated architects. What were their names?

Junctions 5 to 6

1029 Between these junctions the motorway runs alongside Loch Leven. For what fish is the loch especially known?

1030 At the RSPB reserve on the southern shore of the loch, spectacular flights of Pink-footed Geese arrive in October. Where do they breed in summer?

1031 Mary Queen of Scots was imprisoned on Castle Island in the loch in 1567–8. Who helped her to escape, and how?

Junctions 6 to 7

1032 Junction 6 leads into Kinross. Who was elected MP for Kinross in 1963 after a long period in the House of Lords?

Junctions 7 to 8

1033 What is the characteristic form of many Scottish castles?

Junctions 8 to 9

1034 At Junction 8 there is a final view back over Loch Leven. Which is the largest loch in Scotland?

1035 By what name are lochs known in Ireland?

1036 At St Andrews, on the Fife coast to the east, the students elect the Rector of the University. Who is the present Rector?

1037 What is the name of the celebrated golf club at St Andrews, and when was it founded?

Junctions 9 to 10

1038 You are now driving through the Tay valley. How long is the river Tay?

Junctions 10 to 11

1039 Between these junctions the motorway runs along the western edge of Perth. Who wrote *The Fair Maid of Perth*?

1040 Of which Australian state is the city of Perth the capital, and on which river does it stand?

1041 Who was crowned at Scone Palace, a short distance north of Perth, on 1 January 1651?

ANSWERS

A1 (M) HERTFORDSHIRE
1 Kissing hands.
2 Four: Ramsay MacDonald, Clement Attlee, Harold Wilson, James Callaghan.
3 *Oliver Twist*.
4 The Cecils.
5 Queen Elizabeth I.
6 Amy Johnson in her De Havilland Gipsy Moth *Jason* from 5 to 24 May 1930.
7 George Bernard Shaw.
8 Bowes-Lyon.
9 Castle Mey.
10 *A Room With A View* and *A Passage To India*.
11 Sir Nigel Gresley; 1 May 1928.
12 Secretary of State for Education.
13 Roy Jenkins, David Owen, William Rodgers, Shirley Williams.
14 Sir Ebenezer Howard.
15 Oliver Cromwell.
16 Anthony Trollope's *Barchester Towers*.
17 The *Daily Telegraph*.

A1(M) YORKSHIRE
18 He discovered the law of gravitation; invented calculus; and recognized that white light is a mixture of coloured lights which can be separated by refraction.
19 New Jersey.
20 That of the King, Charles I.
21 A medieval sporting event, at which mounted knights in armour would fight with blunted weapons.
22 Garderobe.
23 1776; 1 mile, 6 furlong, 127 yards.
24 A translation of the *Book of Psalms*; the *Luttrell Psalter* is full of illustrations depicting fourteenth-century village life.
25 Prince Rupert commanded the Royalist army, the Earl of Manchester, Lord Fairfax and Lord Leven the Parliamentary forces.

26 In 1066; Harold of England defeated Harald of Norway.

A1(M) NORTH-EAST
27 Lewis Carroll.
28 *Discovery* and *Resolution*.
29 Between the North and South Islands of New Zealand.
30 Harold Macmillan.
31 On Cross Fell, east of Penrith.
32 *Locomotion No. 1*; George Stephenson.
33 On 27 September 1825.
34 Timothy Hackworth.
35 Sir Compton Mackenzie; he was born at West Hartlepool on the coast east of the motorway.
36 It most likely derives from an old manorial custom that allowed tenants to take as much firewood from hedges as they could cut with a crook or bill-hook, and as much low timber from woodland as a shepherd's crook could bring down.
37 In the USA in 1886.
38 Peter Lee (1864–1935), a local man who became President of the Miners' Federation and first chairman of a Labour-controlled County Council.
39 1900; Labour Representation Committee.
40 Arthur Henderson, who joined the coalition government on its formation in 1915.
41 In 1868 at Manchester.
42 On the third Saturday of July.
43 Oxford and Cambridge; London.
44 The Venerable Bede, who is buried in Durham Cathedral.
45 The Wear.
46 Steel.
47 1937 (Sunderland 3, Preston North End 1); 1973 (Sunderland 1, Leeds United 0).
48 John Adams.
49 Olympia.
50 Every four years on the first Tuesday in November; the next elections are due in 1988.
51 White with a red hoop (vest) and red shorts.
52 Daniel Defoe; Man Friday.

M1
53 The Royal Flying Corps and the Royal Naval Service; 1918.
54 15 September.

55 The Midland Railway; in 1868.
56 Stanley Baldwin and Winston Churchill.
57 1964; 1986.
58 Ken Livingstone.
59 The BBC.
60 *Your Song*.
61 He is the head of a monastery.
62 Henry VI.
63 It is Latin for 'of the Danes'; in Anglo-Saxon times this area came under a Danish overlord.
64 Dover, Kent, and Wroxeter, Shropshire.
65 Dromedaries, or Arabian Camels, have one hump and are found in North Africa and in Asia as far east as India; Bactrian Camels have two humps and are natives of Central Asia.
66 The Kodiak Bear.
67 The Giraffe.
68 A thick roll of suet that farm labourers used to take into the fields for their midday meal; fish formed the filling at the start of the roll, then came meat, then jam.
69 In 1959; Nottingham Forest won 2–1.
70 Hats.
71 4 feet 8½ inches, known as standard gauge.
72 1,178,835 portions each week (1983/4).
73 Over 200,000.
74 The Great Exhibition, staged in Hyde Park in 1851.
75 The Dukes of Bedford.
76 Venice.
77 John Bunyan, from 1660 to 1672.
78 Catherine of Aragon; 24 years. After her divorce she lived at Ampthill, now east of the motorway.
79 455 kilometres.
80 1,000 million.
81 The Open University.
82 The Battle of Jutland, 1916.
83 In the Wash, north of Kings Lynn.
84 Three: the Sussex Ouse, the Yorkshire Ouse, and the Little Ouse, which rises in Suffolk and joins the Great Ouse near Ely.
85 William Cowper.
86 To enable housewives to use up all their fat and eggs before the start of Lent the next day, Ash Wednesday.
87 *Crêpes*.
88 They were legged through; the boatmen lay flat on their

backs on planks jutting out over each side of the barge and 'walked' their craft through the tunnel with their legs.

89 Des O'Connor.

90 The Nene.

91 Gian Sammarco.

92 A last.

93 Shoes with wooden sides to which shoe or boot uppers are attached.

94 Henry VI.

95 At Althorp, 4 miles east of the motorway.

96 William Arthur Philip Louis, born on 21 June 1982; and Henry Charles Albert David, born on 15 September 1984.

97 Robert Stephenson; in 1838.

98 The Advanced Passenger Train; the train tilted as it went round bends.

99 62 miles.

100 *Tom Brown's Schooldays*, by Thomas Hughes.

101 Rupert Brooke, who was educated at Rugby School.

102 The word is Celtic for stream or river; the Welsh form is Afon.

103 The Americans Wilbur and Orville Wright in 1903 in their bi-plane *Flyer*.

104 Louis Blériot, in July 1909.

105 John Wycliffe, rector of Lutterworth from 1374 to 1384.

106 It derives from the Old English for ash and the Scandinavian for a habitation.

107 Rutland.

108 At Melton Mowbray, in north-east Leicestershire.

109 Port.

110 The Wars of the Roses; on 22 August 1485.

111 Richard III; the Tudors.

112 The Soar.

113 Thomas Cook.

114 Sue Townsend.

115 The Fosse Way.

116 Hampton Court.

117 Lady Jane Grey, who spent most of her life at Bradgate House, the ruins of which lie east of the motorway at Junction 22.

118 Fallow: buck, doe and fawn. Red: stag, hind and calf.

119 The Ural Mountains in the USSR.

120 Flashing lights that mark pedestrian crossings; they are named after Sir Leslie Hore-Belisha, the Minister of Transport who introduced them in 1934.

121   Hunting.

122   Marylebone.

123   Campanology.

124   A stack.

125   Auto-Union, from Germany.

126   170 miles; five: Staffordshire, Derbyshire, Nottinghamshire, Lincolnshire and Humberside.

127   George Hudson.

128   On the first Wednesday in June at Epsom, Surrey; for three-year-old colts and fillies.

129   Brian Clough.

130   Boots.

131   'General' William Booth.

132   Jayne Torvill and Christopher Dean, who are both from Nottingham.

133   Cricket.

134   *Women in Love*.

135   Mellors, the gamekeeper.

136   Robin Hood.

137   He was the monarch's representative in a shire, and had extensive judicial and executive powers.

138   At Missolonghi in Greece in 1824, fighting with Greek rebels against Turkish rule.

139   A gladiator forced to fight in the Colosseum of Imperial Rome.

140   104.5 million tonnes.

141   To give early warning of the presence of carbon monoxide; their metabolism responds more quickly to the toxic effects than man's.

142   According to legend, Leander, a young man from Abydos on the shore of the Hellespont (Dardanelles), loved Hero, a beautiful priestess who lived on the opposite shore. Leander swam across to his lover at night, Hero holding a torch to show him the way. One stormy night, Leander was drowned, whereupon Hero threw herself into the sea in despair.

143   Chatsworth.

144   The motte, or mound, a fortified strongpoint with a tower on top; and the bailey, an enclosure that contained quarters for animals, workshops and other buildings.

145   The safety lamp, which he developed at the same time as Sir Humphry Davy.

146 A large, double-ended, overstuffed couch.

147 A single-breasted black overcoat worn in the late nineteenth and early twentieth centuries.

148 Pisa, in Italy.

149 Port and starboard; bow and stern.

150 Gold, red, blue, black and white; 9, 7, 5, 3 and 1.

151 Cymru.

152 Three: East, North and West.

153 Winifred Holtby.

154 Cutlery.

155 'Cast' or 'crucible' steel, an absolutely pure steel of uniform quality; his invention laid the foundation of the city's steel industry.

156 1200 miles; the Sea of Azov, an arm of the Black Sea.

157 Mary Queen of Scots.

158 An Australian cricket trophy awarded each season to the premier state team. It was established in the early 1890s by Lord Sheffield, who had taken an English team to Australia.

159 In the Falkland Islands on 4 May 1982; a French-made Exocet air-to-sea missile.

160 Freddie Trueman.

161 Geoffrey Boycott.

162 It is fed into the centre of a pair of millstones. The top stone revolves, the lower one remains stationary. The grain is moved by centrifugal force to the outside edge of the stones, being ground to meal as it goes.

163 Joseph Locke.

164 Michael Parkinson.

165 Paul Simon.

166 From 12 March 1984 to 6 March 1985, the longest industrial dispute in British history; 26.1 million.

167 Arthur Scargill.

168 Clegg, Compo and Foggy.

169 9 December 1960; Violet Carson and Jack Howarth.

170 Evelyn Waugh; John Mortimer.

171 Anthony Andrews, Diana Quick and Jeremy Irons; Sebastian Flyte's teddy bear.

172 Richard, Duke of York.

173 Barbara Hepworth.

174 Medieval plays depicting Biblical events (e.g. the Nativity and the Passion). Each play in the cycle was acted by a different guild.

175 George Gissing.

176 Each bowl is known as a wood; the smaller ball is the jack.

177 The Aire.

178 Don Revie.

179 Cricket, Rugby League and Rugby Union.

M11

180 Thames Ironworks.

181 The Kelmscott Press.

182 Phil Redmond.

183 Sir Winston Churchill.

184 The London Borough of Redbridge.

185 Chelmsford.

186 273; King's Cross, with an estimated 73 million passenger journeys starting and ending there in 1986.

187 The Twopenny Tube.

188 A market.

189 Henry Morton Stanley; the *New York Herald*.

190 Basildon, Bracknell, Crawley, Hatfield, Hemel Hempstead, Stevenage, Welwyn Garden City.

191 They were created, following an Act of Parliament in 1946, as self-contained towns with their own industries and amenities, designed to absorb overspill population from London and thereby relieve the overcrowded inner areas of the capital.

192 Jean Harlow.

193 Philip II of Spain.

194 Bow Bells; that he would become Lord Mayor of London three times.

195 'Bishop's' because the first record of the settlement dates from 1065, when the castle was sold to the Bishops of London; 'Stortford' because travellers could cross the river Stort there.

196 Ian Smith; Zimbabwe.

197 A flitch, or side, of bacon awarded to a newly-wed couple able to swear – and prove – that they had lived together amicably for a year and a day, without quarrelling and without wishing themselves unmarried!

198 7 to 8 million.

199 The Granta.

200 Lancelot; because he used to remark that he could see 'capabilities' in the estates he was commissioned to improve.

201 As a medicine, a dye, and a flavouring for food.

202 Butcher's apprentice.

203 The circulation of the blood.

204 The Icknield Way.

205 1622; the name is taken from a nickname of Charles II, which in turn derives from the name of his favourite horse.

206 The One Thousand Guineas and the Two Thousand Guineas.

207 Flying Fortress and Superfortress.

208 She carried the first atomic bomb dropped on Japan in 1945.

209 After the now vanished figure of Gogmagog, a mythical giant chieftain from the west of England, carved in the chalk.

210 On the Thames between Putney and Mortlake in west London.

211 'Stands the Church clock at ten to three?
   And is there honey still for tea?'

212 Jesus College.

213 Henry VI.

M18

214 The Benedictine Order.

215 At Cîteaux, near Dijon, in France.

216 Sydney Smith.

217 A cricket ball that pitches 3 or 4 feet from the wicket, immediately in front of it.

218 Four: at Bradford, Leeds, Sheffield and York.

219 Danum.

220 The Lincoln Handicap, which nowadays is run at Doncaster.

221 As the official residence of the Lord Mayor of London.

222 Pantograph.

223 The Great Northern Railway.

224 A4.

225 1968.

226 Dark blue, light blue and gold.

227 1863.

228 The trophy for which England and Australia compete in each Test Match series. The ashes are those of a cricket ball burnt by a group of disappointed Melbourne ladies when the home side lost to an English touring team in 1883. Whoever wins the series, the Ashes remain in an urn at Lord's Cricket Ground in London.

229 46.

M180

230 £91 million.

231 On 22 January 1966; a by-election in a marginal seat in Hull which the government wanted to hold.

232 The Methodist Church.

233 'Hark! The Herald Angels Sing'.

234 York Minster and St Paul's Cathedral.

235 The Republican Party.

236 Alfred, Lord Tennyson.

237 Sudbury, Suffolk.

238 Ian Botham.

239 Kevin Keegan and Ray Clemence.

240 George Stubbs; some of the studies for the book were done in Horkstow, north of the motorway.

241 Ermine Street.

242 Frederick Delius.

243 A sailing vessel with two masts both carrying square sails.

244 The Lincolnshire Wolds.

245 Skegness.

M2

246 *Great Expectations*, *The Uncommercial Traveller*, *Our Mutual Friend* and *The Mystery of Edwin Drood*.

247 On the Beaufort Scale; Force 11.

248 The Dutch fleet raided and set fire to several vessels of the English fleet.

249 Henry VIII.

250 HMS *Victory*.

251 William Pitt the Elder.

252 The Royal Engineers.

253 David Frost.

254 Colin Cowdrey.

255 1018.

256 The Swale.

257 Island of Sheep.

258 Philippa of Hainault, who married Edward III in 1328.

259 James II.

260 Honorary knighthood.

261 *Do They Know It's Christmas?*

262 Oysters.

263 Thomas à Becket; T.S. Eliot, *Murder in the Cathedral*.

264 Matthew Arnold.

M20

265 Maidstone.

266 Queen Victoria.

267 The Earl of St Andrews, Lady Helen Windsor and Lord Nicholas Windsor.

268 2 miles, 1144 yards.

269 A black-and-white chequered flag.

270 Span.

271 Winchester and Canterbury; because in the Middle Ages pilgrims used it to travel to the shrine of Thomas à Becket at Canterbury.

272 22.

273 'Trosley'.

274 Wat Tyler.

275 A covered seat carried on poles by two bearers back and front.

276 A barn used for holding the parson's tithe, that is, the payment received of a tenth of the annual agricultural produce of his parish.

277 70 miles.

278 A Man of Kent is born east of the Medway, whereas a Kentish Man is from west Kent.

279 The 750-volt DC third-rail system.

280 Ledia or Leed, chief minister of King Ethelbert of Kent and brother of King Alfred the Great.

281 Aphra Behn, who was born in Wye, a few miles north of the motorway.

282 A building stone found on the Kent coast.

283 Hythe and Rye; as part of the coastal defences in the Napoleonic Wars.

284 15-inch.

285 E.E. Nesbit; she is buried at St Mary in the Marsh on Romney Marsh.

286 Dover, Hastings, Romney and Sandwich.

287 The Queen Mother.

288 *Civilization*.

289 At the east end of the Strait of Dover, where it joins the North Sea; 21 miles.

290 *La Manche*, meaning 'the sleeve'.

M23

291 At the Oval Cricket Ground, Kennington, south London;

the Duchy of Cornwall.

292 61,237, an average of 50.65 per match.

293 *Pride and Prejudice* by Jane Austen.

294 Brightelmston.

295 John Nash.

296 It started in Pudding Lane and finished at Pie Corner, on the corner of Cock Lane and Giltspur Street.

297 117.

298 Over 50,000.

299 116.3 hours per year on average; October is the most foggy month, July the least.

300 Most probably because the place was an especially muddy stretch of road, like pease pottage (a mash of boiled dried peas eaten with pork) in consistency.

M25

301 Thamesmead.

302 Richard Trevithick who is buried at Dartford.

303 June 1970 to March 1974; Margaret Thatcher.

304 Constantine.

305 Billie-Jean King; she has won 6 singles, 10 doubles and 4 mixed titles.

306 Australia, Flushing Meadow (USA), Paris and Wimbledon.

307 Samuel Palmer.

308 The Sackvilles.

309 Charles Darwin, who lived at Downe, north of the motorway.

310 General James Wolfe.

311 Chartwell.

312 First Lord of the Admiralty.

313 Iron Curtain, used to characterize the western frontiers of the Communist-controlled states of Eastern Europe.

314 18,800 tons from 7 September 1940 to 11 May 1941.

315 Secretary to the Admiralty.

316 Archbishop Cranmer. It was first used at a service in Warlingham parish church, now north of the motorway.

317 Farnham, Surrey, and Dover, Kent.

318 Lord Howard of Effingham. He is buried in the vaults of St Mary Magdalene Church, Reigate.

319 The river Mole.

320 Thomas Malthus.

321 As a laxative.

322   The Coronation Cup and the Oaks.

323   Sir Lewis Casson.

324   The Old Vic and Sadler's Wells.

325   Louis-Philippe, King of France.

326   Princess Charlotte, who died in childbirth at Claremont.

327   Paul Getty.

328   Alliott Berdon Roe, founder of the Avro Company (now part of British Aerospace), who built his biplane in the first aeroshed in Britain and made his first successful test flight at Brooklands in December 1907.

329   Mahomet; the *Koran*.

330   The pilgrimage to Mecca that every Muslim hopes to make once in his lifetime.

331   Henry VI.

332   The Duke of Windsor.

333   J.F. Kennedy.

334   Over 22,600.

335   Four million bottles.

336   Sir Allen Lane.

337   *Ariel* by André Maurois, on 30 July 1935.

338   32, plus the City of London.

339   *Elegy Written in a Country Churchyard*, by Thomas Gray.

340   Tom Stoppard, who lives at Iver, west of the motorway. The play was called *Rosencrantz And Guildenstern Are Dead*.

341   Two crossed keys, because he was entrusted with the 'keys to the kingdom of heaven' (Matthew 16,19).

342   At Karakakoa Bay, Hawaii.

343   Heart transplants.

344   The Chess, Colne and Gade.

345   Everton; Watford lost 2–0.

346   6,690,008 (1981).

347   Six; Buckinghamshire, Essex, Greater London, Hertfordshire, Kent and Surrey.

348   Dr Johnson.

349   Shelley in *Peter Bell The Third*.

350   Nicholas Breakspear, who became Hadrian IV. He was born in Abbots Langley, south of the motorway.

351   Verulamium.

352   A warrior-queen of the Iceni, the people of Norfolk and Suffolk. She took London and St Albans and put to death many thousands of Romans before the Roman governor of Britain succeeded in defeating her.

353   The first British martyr, killed in 305 while sheltering a Christian priest.

354   The Wooden Wonder; over 400 mph.

355   The Saxon *baernet*, 'a burning', i.e. an area cleared in a forest by fire. In Saxon times this area was thickly wooded.

356   The Earl of Warwick, leader of the Lancastrian forces.

357   A broad belt of farmland, parkland and recreation ground established around London in the 1930s, in which all development is strictly regulated, in order to block the rapid spread of the capital into the countryside and to provide easy access to the country for city-dwellers.

358   The Piccadilly Line.

359   On the coast of Australia, south of Sydney.

360   Henry Mayhew, who lived at Botany Bay.

361   Eleanor of Castile, wife of Edward I; the crosses were erected at the resting-places of the coffin on its journey to Westminster Abbey.

362   At the junction of Fleet Street and Strand; the western boundary of the City of London.

363   At Blackwall.

364   Harold II, who lost the throne of England to William the Conqueror.

365   1884.

366   France and Spain.

367   The Corporation of London.

368   The capture of Cadiz in 1596.

369   In the Tower of London on 25 February 1601, after he had tried to raise the City of London against Elizabeth I.

370   Catherine of Aragon (divorced); Anne Boleyn (beheaded); Jane Seymour (died two weeks after childbirth).

371   Alan Michael Sugar Trading.

372   The binary system.

373   36.

374   1¼ miles.

375   About 88 minutes; 41 stations.

376   100,000 to 10,000 years ago; it is called Wurm Glaciation in Europe, Wisconsin Glaciation in North America.

377   Chinese Gordon, because he led the force that put down the Taiping Rebellion in China in 1863–4.

378   1886.

379   14,205 (1986).

380   Westminster Bridge.

381 It was re-erected at Lake Havasu City, Arizona, USA.
382 Two: the Blackwall and Rotherhithe Tunnels.

M27

383 William II.
384 92,773 acres; the Court of Verderers, which meets at Lyndhurst.
385 The Test and the Itchen; the motorway crosses the Test between Junctions 2 and 3.
386 Lord Mountbatten of Burma, who lived at Broadlands, near Romsey, north of the motorway.
387 There are double tides; i.e. four low and four high tides every 24 hours, instead of the usual two.
388 1513.
389 King Cnut, or Canute; to demonstrate to flattering courtiers that he could *not* command the waves – that even a king must accept limits to his authority.
390 The *Supermarine Spitfire*.
391 Sir John Millais.
392 The Fastnet Race; Cowes, round the Isles of Scilly to the Fastnet Rock, and back to Plymouth.
393 Queen Victoria and Prince Albert.
394 6 June 1944.
395 Mulberry.
396 Cricket.
397 Henry V.
398 King Henry VIII's sister.
399 On 19 July 1545; all but 40 of the 700 men on board.
400 Flagship of the Commander-in-Chief, Naval Home Command.
401 'Thank God, I have done my duty.'
402 Pompey.

M3

403 The Rugby Football Union.
404 Thomas Wolsey.
405 County of the Middle Saxons.
406 Lord's.
407 June; The Gold Cup.
408 A celebrated firm of horse auctioneers.
409 Anders Celsius; 1742; Swedish.
410 A discharge of static electricity, usually either between a

cloud and the ground, or between two clouds.

411 Shooting.

412 King Hussein of Jordan and the Sultan of Oman.

413 The first officially-recognized powered flight in the UK.

414 Napoleon III.

415 In 1854.

416 Nepal.

417 Charles Kingsley, who is buried at Eversley, a few miles north of the motorway.

418 Hertford and Hereford.

419 *Pygmalion*, by George Bernard Shaw.

420 *Peter Pan* by J.M. Barrie.

421 Runnymede.

422 Usually during the day, hanging upside down in a cave or other dark place.

423 2,798,101.

424 *Ruddigore*.

425 *Emma*.

426 Sarah Ferguson; HRH the Princess Andrew, Duchess of York.

427 Watercress.

428 John Arlott.

429 Wykehamists, after William of Wykeham, who founded the school in 1382.

430 15 July; it will rain for forty days in succession.

431 King Cnut, or Canute.

432 New Vaudeville Band.

M4

433 Augusta, Dowager Princess of Wales, in 1759.

434 The Dukes of Northumberland.

435 Rod Stewart.

436 528,775 tonnes.

437 500,000.

438 31,421,379 million (1985–86); 68, plus 2 cargo.

439 31 May 1946.

440 By 'puddling', that is by stamping 'puddle', a mixture of sand, clay and water, into the canal bed.

441 John Betjeman: 'Come friendly bombs, and fall on Slough!'

442 Henry VI.

443 Mrs Wallis Simpson.

444 Jane Seymour, his third, who died two weeks after giving birth to a son.

445 The Queen Mother.

446 210 miles; at Thames Head near Cirencester, Gloucestershire.

447 Edmund Spenser.

448 George, Harris, and 'I', the book's narrator; Montmorency the dog.

449 The Astors.

450 In 1839; 1 mile 550 yards.

451 A coxswain; in the stern.

452 Alexander Pope.

453 Biscuits.

454 Oscar Wilde.

455 Henry I.

456 The Thames and the Kennet.

457 Copenhagen.

458 Aspley House, at Hyde Park Corner.

459 Lord Warden of the Cinque Ports.

460 *The Wind in the Willows* by Kenneth Grahame.

461 Protest marches from Aldermaston, the headquarters of the Atomic Weapons Research Establishment, to London organized every Easter between 1958 and 1963 to protest at the development of an independent British nuclear deterrent.

462 Calleva Atrebatum.

463 An open square lined by porticoes, shops and offices where trade, political and judicial business was carried on.

464 Leningrad.

465 Greenham Common.

466 Horse-racing.

467 Two years.

468 The Lincoln Handicap (Doncaster) and the Grand National (Liverpool); the Cambridgeshire and the Cesarewitch (both at Newmarket).

469 Dick Francis.

470 Twenty months.

471 King Alfred.

472 The second Tuesday after Easter. In Hungerford, south of Junction 14, the Court that traditionally regulates the rights of common and fishing meets on Hock Tuesday.

473 Eurydice.

474 Catherine of Braganza; Portugal.

475 Tom Brown of *Tom Brown's Schooldays* by Thomas Hughes.

476 Reading and Salisbury.

477 A magical smith who made miraculous swords and created for himself a pair of wings with which to escape his enemies. Legend has it that if a traveller tied up his horse here and went out of sight, leaving a coin, he would find the horse shod on his return.

478 For burying the dead.

479 St George.

480 The Ridge Way.

481 John Churchill.

482 Blenheim.

483 W.H. Smith.

484 The hill on which swine were kept.

485 *King George V*.

486 Isambard Kingdom Brunel; 30 June 1841.

487 During the late Neolithic period, i.e. *c*.2000–1600 BC.

488 In 880; by King Alfred.

489 Athelstan, who is said to have been buried in Malmesbury Abbey.

490 George Washington; his ancestors lived near Malmesbury in the sixteenth century.

491 Abraham Lincoln; his mother came from an old Malmesbury family.

492 Thomas Hobbes, who was born in Malmesbury.

493 Henry Fox Talbot, who lived at Lacock, now south of Junction 17.

494 Jurassic limestone.

495 Wool.

496 Over 22,000.

497 The Dukes of Beaufort.

498 First day: dressage; second day: speed, endurance and cross-country; third day: show jumping.

499 A shuttlecock.

500 Richard 'Beau' Nash.

501 Sir Isaac Pitman, while he was living in Bath.

502 A plain biscuit, often eaten with cheese; Dr William Oliver (1695–1764) was a local physician and an expert on gout.

503 Sir William Herschel, in 1781, while he was living in Bath.

504 A sugared currant bun.

505 Two; Bristol City and Bristol Rovers; in 1909, when City lost 1–0 to Manchester United.

506 Edinburgh.

507 Tony Benn.

508 The SS *Great Britain*.

509 1886.

510 3240 feet; 400 feet.

511 The Wye.

512 William Wordsworth.

513 'Favoured place' or 'market place', from the Latin *vendere*, to sell.

514 Flour, eggs, sugar, baking powder, salt, butter, lard, mace and milk.

515 A seaweed served chiefly in Wales as a vegetable, usually with roast leg of lamb or lobster.

516 Plaid Cymru; two.

517 St David.

518 A tax-collector.

519 Iron ore, limestone and coal.

520 The Second Augustan Legion; between 5000 and 6000 men.

521 For military exercises and displays, gladiatorial contests, animal-baiting and hunting scenes.

522 The Usk.

523 W.H. Davies.

524 Neil Kinnock.

525 A nineteenth-century romantic poet whose real name was William Thomas.

526 Balaclava; Lord Cardigan.

527 Eight.

528 1955.

529 Machynlleth.

530 Lieutenant Bowers, Petty Officer Evans, Captain Oates, Dr Wilson.

531 Roald Amundsen, of Norway.

532 William Burges; between 1865 and 1885.

533 Rugby Union.

534 At the 1958 Commonwealth Games, held in Cardiff.

535 'Ich dien'.

536 On Tower Hill, London.

537 About 560 million.

538 About 1,151 million (1984–5).

539 George Thomas, Speaker of the House of Commons, 1976–83.

540   Morgannwg.

541   19 per cent; about 1 per cent.

542   Snowdon; 3560 feet.

543   A red dragon on a green and white field.

544   At Caernarfon Castle in 1969.

545   Port of sea-kale; sea-kale is thought once to have grown in the area.

546   140 million tonnes (1985–6).

547   Australia, Brazil, Canada, Mauritania and South Africa.

548   464 acres.

549   Anthony Hopkins.

550   Richard Burton.

551   Trinity House.

552   Dylan Thomas, who was born and educated in Swansea.

553   The horse-drawn Oystermouth Railway, on 25 March 1807; the line ran from Swansea to Oystermouth.

554   The Tawe.

555   Gary Sobers, who was playing for Nottinghamshire.

556   Uprisings by the rural poor of South Wales in the 1840s, chiefly against high toll charges. The rioters invaded Carmarthen in 1843.

557   Oil refining.

558   Henry VII.

559   A festival of Welsh literature and culture, in which bards and minstrels compete for prizes in literature, music and drama.

560   They are river boats made of willow and hazel and used for netting salmon and sea trout; a few are still used on the river Teifi around Cilgerran.

561   174.88 mph in 1927, by Malcolm Campbell.

562   J.G. Parry-Thomas.

563   Richard Noble, an Englishman who drove his car *Thrust 2* at an average speed of 1019.44 km/h on the mud flats of the Black Rock Desert, Nevada, USA.

564   Britain was invaded for the last time, by a force of 1400 French convicts under the command of an Irish-American general. They surrendered after two days.

M40

565   Leicester Square; 165 feet 6 inches.

566   *Paradise Lost* by John Milton.

567   William Penn, who is buried at Jordans, north of the motorway; Penn's woods.

568 Connecticut; Delaware; Georgia; Maryland; Massachusetts; New Hampshire; New Jersey; New York; North Carolina; Rhode Island; South Carolina; Virginia.

569 Father Brown; G.K. Chesterton.

570 Sir Stanley Spencer.

571 Furniture-making.

572 Benjamin Disraeli.

573 Mary Godwin, who lived at Marlowe, now south of Junction 4, with her husband, the poet Shelley, in 1817.

574 The Dashwoods.

575 A nominal 'office of profit under the Crown' offered to an MP who wishes to retire from the House of Commons between general elections.

576 Chalk.

577 Coombe Hill, 852 feet.

578 Chequers; Lord Lee of Fareham.

579 Ship money.

580 Bernard Weatherill.

581 The Sorbonne in Paris.

582 Forty.

583 Wide baggy flannel trousers fashionable in Oxford in the 1920s.

584 A sportsman or woman at Oxford or Cambridge University who has been chosen to represent the university in a sport such as cricket, rowing or rugby.

585 Hugh Latimer and Nicholas Ridley, who were among the chief promoters of the Protestant Reformation in England.

M5

586 Mrs Elton in Jane Austen's *Emma*.

587 Ten times: in 1886, 1887, 1888, 1892, 1895, 1912, 1931, 1935, 1954 and 1968. The team won in 1888, 1892, 1931, 1954 and 1968.

588 Sir Edward Burne-Jones.

589 Thomas Newcomen; to pump water from mines.

590 Bournville.

591 Jasper Carrott.

592 George II and George III; Frederick lived from 1707 to 1751, dying before his father.

593 Four times: in 1868, 1880, 1886 and 1892; Benjamin Disraeli.

594 Four: in Dorset–Hampshire, Essex–Suffolk, Oxfordshire–Warwickshire and Kent.

595 Carpets.

596 August 1959.

597 A.E. Housman, author of *A Shropshire Lad*.

598 Literally, a prefabricated house; small homes, usually one-storey, erected on bomb sites and vacant land during and after World War Two to provide temporary housing.

599 A well-insulated underground structure in which ice was stored in the days before refrigeration.

600 In the Trojan War; by an arrow which struck him in his heel, the only unprotected part of his body.

601 Its brine, which, containing 2½ lb of salt per gallon, is ten times saltier than sea water.

602 The *Mayflower*; 1620.

603 King John.

604 The King's.

605 Edward Elgar.

606 Gloucester and Hereford.

607 Apples.

608 Lea and Perrins; vinegar, molasses, sugar, shallots, anchovies, tamarinds, garlic, salt, spices and natural flavouring.

609 Pectin.

610 Henry III's son Edward defeated and killed Simon de Montfort, who was heading a force of rebel barons.

611 991 feet.

612 Samuel Weller.

613 Edward IV and the House of York; the Wars of the Roses.

614 Mustard; in *Henry IV Part II*, Falstaff says of Poins that 'his wit is as thick as Tewkesbury mustard'.

615 The Severn and the Warwickshire Avon.

616 Catherine Parr, his sixth and last.

617 Annually in March; 3 miles 2 furlongs; 12 stone, with a 5 lb allowance for mares.

618 A Great Western Railway express from Cheltenham to London, which for three years in the 1930s was claimed as the world's fastest train.

619 Belgium.

620 Gustav Holst.

621 Architect.

622 They are all characters in stories by Beatrix Potter.

623 He 'stepped in a puddle right up to his middle, and never went there again'.

624 All the animals of the city sang the old Christmas rhymes; tradition has it that beasts can talk in the hours around midnight on Christmas Eve.

625 Robert Raikes.

626 Because it was originally made in the early summer, when milk was richest and most plentiful. Single Gloucester was thin and often made from semi-skimmed milk.

627 W.G. Grace.

628 Scarlet.

629 Princess Anne, Mark Phillips and their family.

630 According to Greek tradition, Judas Iscariot hanged himself on one of these trees; it flowers before the leaves appear.

631 Sir Peter Scott.

632 On the far northern tundra of the USSR.

633 By the bill pattern of black and yellow.

634 Edward II.

635 Vaccination.

636 California.

637 'Who is like the Lord'.

638 The Prince and Princess of Wales and their family.

639 210 miles; on the north-east slope of Plynlimmon in central Wales.

640 A series of tidal waves created by the funnel shape of the estuary; its maximum height, reached at the spring and autumn equinox, is about 9 feet.

641 In the Tower of London; for alleged infidelity.

642 Great Britain and France; 2 March 1969; 16 aircraft starting on 21 January 1976.

643 The Tupolev Tu–144, the world's first supersonic transport aircraft, which first flew on 31 December 1968.

644 The North-West Passage; the North American mainland; the *Matthew*.

645 Methodical and orderly.

646 Harveys.

647 Isambard Kingdom Brunel; 245 feet.

648 Cary Grant.

649 *Vanity Fair*.

650 *In Memoriam*.

651 Edith Cavell, who went to school in Clevedon.

652 Steep Holm and Flat Holm.

653 Basil and Sybil Fawlty.

654 A Norwegian Blue.

655 Guglielmo Marconi, in 1901. Four years earlier he had sent messages across the Bristol Channel from Brean Down, east of the motorway, to Wales – at that time the longest distance over water that a wireless message had been sent.

656 A cave is a natural cavity in rock; a pothole is a vertical shaft.

657 A stalagmite grows upwards, a stalactite downwards.

658 Carboniferous limestone.

659 457 feet.

660 William, the third son of George III, who came to the throne as William IV in 1830.

661 Between Alfred, King of Wessex, and the Danes.

662 Joseph of Arimathaea; the chalice used at the Last Supper.

663 King Arthur.

664 The Parrett.

665 Admiral Sir Robert Blake.

666 The Scilly Isles and Jersey, both of which were taken by Admiral Blake.

667 The Quantocks.

668 Samuel Taylor Coleridge.

669 Charles II's eldest, illegitimate, son, who was trying to overthrow James II.

670 The trial of Monmouth's followers, who were hanged, transported, whipped and fined; Judge Jeffreys.

671 In Strand, London; the Inland Revenue.

672 Osier.

673 Applejack, calvados and cider.

674 A Flemish-born impostor who was the focus of a Yorkist plot against Henry VII. He landed in Cornwall in 1497 and advanced with 6000 followers through Taunton.

675 Joel Garner and Viv Richards.

676 The Blackdown Hills.

677 175 feet.

678 St Helena.

679 Chatsworth House, Derbyshire.

680 Sir Henry Newbolt in *Drake's Drum*.

681 The march from Mendelssohn's *Midsummer Night's Dream*.

682 R.D. Blackmore.

683 The trench that brings water to a mill-wheel.

684 A woollen fabric made from well-twisted yarn spun of long-staple wool; from the village of Worsted in Norfolk.

685   The Culm.

686   Broad gauge: that is, a 7-foot gauge.

687   God's Wonderful Railway, and, when the company lost its identity in the 1923 Grouping, Gone With Regret; Great Way Round (because the GWR's first line from London to Devon and Cornwall took a northerly route through Bristol).

688   2385.

689   Sir George Carew; the Carew family owned Bickleigh Castle, now north-west of the motorway.

690   William Makepeace Thackeray.

691   To provide a constant supply of pure spring water.

692   *Semper Fidelis*, 'Ever Faithful', said to have been suggested by Elizabeth I in recognition of the city's loyalty.

693   Archbishop William Temple.

694   A traditional Arab trading vessel normally fitted with triangular lateen sails; in the Indian Ocean and the Red Sea.

695   Captain William Bligh; with 18 others he was set adrift in an open boat after the crew of the *Bounty* had mutinied, and eventually landed at Timor, near Java, six weeks later, having sailed for over 3600 miles. He is a forebear of the Countess of Devon, who lives at Powderham Castle, near Junction 31.

M50

696   *Enigma Variations*.

697   Three: two for the volin and one for the 'cello.

698   He was the first person to extol the medicinal virtues of Malvern Water.

699   Worcestershire Beacon; 1394 feet.

700   Beer; oast-house.

701   'Tyne coal, road-rail, pig-lead, firewood, iron-ware, and cheap tin trays'; she was 'butting through the Channel in the mad March days'.

702   Cecil Day Lewis.

703   Wimpole Street.

704   In a mews.

705   Pointers and setters.

706   About 85 mph.

707   Supposedly because he wore black armour in battle.

708   130 miles; on the east slope of Plynlimmon in central Wales.

709   Lawrence of Arabia.

710   Second-hand books.

M54

711 Charles II, after his defeat at the Battle of Worcester in 1651.

712 Henry Percy, known as Hotspur.

713 HMS *Beagle*.

714 An earthwork marking the Welsh border, put up by Offa, King of Mercia, in the eighth century.

715 The Bluebell Railway.

716 The Ffestiniog Railway.

717 Frank (later Sir Frank) Whittle; on 12 April 1937.

718 The Gloster Whittle E.28/39; 15 May 1941.

719 The Soviet cosmonaut Yuri Gagarin.

720 Fort William and Inverness.

721 St Katharine's Docks.

722 China.

723 Abraham Darby II.

724 1334 feet.

M55

725 518 feet 9 inches, to the top of the flagstaff.

726 375,000 light bulbs and 75 miles of wiring and cable.

727 14,483,000 (1985).

728 The USA; 3,166,000.

729 Golf.

730 Ernie stands for Electronic Random Number Indicator Equipment. He selects the winning number in each month's draw for Premium Savings Bonds. His office is at Lytham St Anne's.

731 The Wyre.

732 Stan Mortensen.

733 Alan Ball.

M6

734 Fifteen and thirteen respectively.

735 Win all four matches in the annual Five Nations Championship between England, France, Ireland, Scotland and Wales.

736 Thomas Arnold.

737 Exeter and Lincoln.

738 The raised earth embankment on which Roman roads were often built.

739 A habit.

740 Lady Godiva. Her husband Leofric promised to relieve the citizens of Coventry of the heavy taxes he had imposed on them if she would ride naked through the streets of the city – which she did. Leofric kept his promise.

741 They are ignored, and people refuse to talk to them.

742 Sir Basil Spence; Graham Sutherland.

743 An early bicycle with a large driving wheel (the penny) and a small rear wheel (the farthing) that acted as a stabilizer. Coventry was the first centre of the British cycle industry.

744 A Daimler, made in Coventry and bought by the Prince of Wales, later Edward VII, in 1900.

745 George Eliot; she was born at Arbury, north of the motorway.

746 Sir Arthur Wellesley, later the Duke of Wellington; France.

747 111 miles; over 3000 buses.

748 The International Motor Show.

749 1,006,908 (1981).

750 Neville Chamberlain.

751 100 miles.

752 Pebble Mill.

753 Spaghetti alla bolognese is served with a meat sauce, spaghetti napolitana with a tomato sauce.

754 Green.

755 Two: Birmingham City and Aston Villa.

756 Lloyds and the Midland.

757 £225.

758 Jerome K. Jerome.

759 The Saddlers, because the town was once famous for leather-working.

760 Woden, the principal Anglo-Saxon god, of war, learning and poetry.

761 Lock-making.

762 Billy Wright; 105 caps.

763 Enoch Powell.

764 Thomas Brassey.

765 It is short for 'navigator' and was originally employed to describe the men who built the canals in the late eighteenth century.

766 Aneurin Bevan.

767 The Emperor Claudius; at Richborough, Kent, in AD 43.

768 A tract of unenclosed land reserved for breeding and hunting game.

769 The Commonwealth War Graves Commission; 23,465.

770 The execution of 4250 Polish officers in Katyn Forest, near

Smolensk, USSR, almost certainly by Soviet forces.

771 51 to 62 lb.

772 *The Compleat Angler;* ecclesiastical biographies.

773 A castle is 'slighted'.

774 Mrs Malaprop in *The Rivals*.

775 At the south-western tip of Portugal.

776 Robert Browning.

777 Publilius Syrus.

778 Mick Jagger, Brian Jones, Keith Richard, Charlie Watts and Bill Wyman.

779 The Palace of Westminster.

780 Etruria.

781 Kiln.

782 He uses a lump of clay to make a pot on a wheel.

783 R.J. Mitchell.

784 1949.

785 Burslem, Fenton, Hanley, Longton, Stoke and Tunstall.

786 Arnold Bennett.

787 *Alice in Wonderland*; its smile.

788 Over 6 million; 415.

789 Birmingham; London; Mr Porter.

790 Silver Ghost.

791 Primitive Methodism.

792 For exercise, especially in poor weather, and to display a collection of paintings.

793 Bear-baiting.

794 The Shropshire Union Canal; the Trent & Mersey Canal; and the rivers Dane and Weaver.

795 250 feet.

796 Neutron stars of enormous density, formed following the gravitational collapse of old stars.

797 Salt.

798 Canal barges, between the river Weaver and the Trent & Mersey Canal above it.

799 Ludwig Mond and Sir John Brunner; Imperial Chemical Industries.

800 Cranford.

801 *Wives and Daughters*; Cumnor Towers.

802 James, Lewis, Matthew Digby and Samuel.

803 Ornamental plaster-work.

804 Alice Liddell.

805 The March Hare, the Mad Hatter, the Dormouse and Alice.

806 1894; 35.5 miles.

807 The Goyt and the Etherow.

808 Gerry and the Pacemakers.

809 926,293 (1981).

810 William Huskisson, a prominent Tory politician and MP for Liverpool.

811 Silica (sand), sodium carbonate (soda) and calcium carbonate (limestone).

812 The third or fourth week in March and the first or second week in November.

813 George Formby.

814 A landing-stage on the Leeds & Liverpool Canal.

815 George Orwell.

816 Steve Heighway.

817 A flight is a group of locks with a short stretch of water between each; a staircase is a sequence of connected locks, in which the bottom gate of one lock also forms the top gate of the next lock, and so on.

818 Lindisfarne, off the Northumberland coast.

819 Village of the cross; the base of a medieval market cross can still be seen in the village.

820 'Stern ruler'.

821 Euston and Glasgow Central.

822 1848; 1974.

823 Trucks.

824 Sir Michael Edwardes.

825 Sir Henry Tate.

826 The Ribble.

827 Weaving.

828 Cromwell decisively defeated a superior Royalist force.

829 Nobby Stiles.

830 Francis Thompson; the words are his own.

831 Savoury cakes sprinkled with caraway seeds.

832 Sheep and cattle fairs.

833 2 February; the feast of the Purification of the Virgin Mary.

834 64,679 (1981); Douglas.

835 The Court of Tynwald; the House of Keys.

836 The Tourist Trophy (TT) motor-cycle races.

837 They have no tail.

838 A strip of linen on which can be seen the image of a crucified man, thought by experts to be Jesus Christ.

839 The Lune.

840 Her Majesty the Queen.

841 Gillows; the present-day store is Waring and Gillows.

842 The Society of Friends.

843 *Brief Encounter*.

844 LMS Class 5MT 4–6–0 No. 44871. She is preserved in the Steamtown Railway Museum, Carnforth.

845 Buff streaked with dark brown; like a foghorn.

846 The west coast of Africa.

847 An arbour or covered walk formed of growing plants trained over trellis-work.

848 The art of clipping and trimming shrubs and hedges into ornamental or fantastic shapes.

849 The border dispute between Canada and the USA, especially in the region of the Great Lakes.

850 Catherine Parr, the last, who survived him.

851 K Shoes and Kendal mint-cake.

852 A green woollen cloth worn by medieval archers.

853 A. Wainwright.

854 Scafell Pike, 3206 feet; Helvellyn, 3116 feet; Skiddaw, 3054 feet.

855 Mrs William Heelis.

856 A washerwoman.

857 His shoes and his jacket; in Mr McGregor's garden.

858 The National Trust.

859 Lake Windermere.

860 John Ruskin, who lived at Brantwood from 1872 until his death in 1900.

861 Dove Cottage.

862 *The Prelude*, Book XI; the French Revolution.

863 Harrison Stickle, 2403 feet, and Pike O'Stickle, 2323 feet.

864 Kirkstone Pass, 1476 feet, between Ullswater and Windermere.

865 Manchester.

866 Arthur Ransome.

867 John Susan, Titty and Roger Walker, and Nancy and Peggy Blackett; Wild Cat Island.

868 Kanchenjunga, the third highest mountain in the world.

869 Seathwaite, Borrowdale; 122.8 inches.

870 Herdwicks.

871 *The Herries Chronicle*.

872 Robert Southey.

873 John Peel; grey.

874 Chris Bonington, who lives in Caldbeck.

875 William Augustus, 3rd Duke of Cumberland and second son of George II. He earned his nickname because of the brutal manner in which he crushed the Young Pretender's uprising in 1745.

876 They are dry-salted for three weeks and then hung in the kitchen rafters.

877 Each fighter stands with his hands clasped behind the neck and shoulders of his opponent. The first person to unclasp his hands or touch the ground with any part of his body is the loser.

878 The Midland Railway; to gain its own direct route to Scotland.

879 Dent, further south on the Settle to Carlisle line.

880 The Caldew, Eden and Petteril.

881 The Prime Minister lives at number 10, the Chancellor of the Exchequer at number 11; number 12 is the office of the Government Chief Whip.

882 Luguvalium.

883 Caledonian; Glasgow & South Western; London & North Western; Maryport & Carlisle; Midland; North British; North Eastern.

884 73 miles; Bowness on the Solway Firth and Wallsend on the river Tyne; as a permanent defence against Pictish invaders from the north, and to mark the northern limit of the Roman Empire.

885 Edward I, in 1307.

886 George Bernard Shaw in *The Apple Cart*.

M62

887 The Cavern Club; Pete Best, George Harrison, John Lennon, Paul McCartney and Stu Sutcliffe.

888 Bill Shankly.

889 Harold Wilson.

890 After a gnarled ash tree that grew in the village, which until about 1700 was known simply as Ash; Ken Dodd.

891 The Owl and the Pussy-Cat; 'some honey, and plenty of money, wrapped up in a five-pound note'; 'the land where the Bong-tree grows'.

892 13 feet; 6½ tons; 21 months.

893 *Rocket*; Robert Stephenson.

894 Wapping (freight) and Crown Street (passengers) in Liverpool; Liverpool Road in Manchester.

895 Juniper berries, coriander seed, angelica root, lemon peel, liquorice, almonds, cassia bark, orris, water and alcohol.

896 4.5 million litres.

897 Russia; grain.

898 Decayed vegetable matter compacted in an oxygen-deficient environment.

899 Rhododendrons, azaleas and heathers.

900 Arms, ammunition and other military equipment.

901 Merseyside; South Yorkshire; Tyne and Wear; West Midlands; West Yorkshire.

902 Pastry, butter, sugar, currants, peel, nutmeg and spice.

903 A bridge carrying water, often a canal; the word comes from the Latin *aqua* (water) and *ducere* (to lead).

904 James Brindley.

905 Matt Busby.

906 C.P. Scott.

907 The Halle.

908 Brian Robson, whom Manchester United bought from West Bromwich Albion for £1.5 million in 1981.

909 Joe Mercer; Leicester City; 1–0.

910 The annual closure of factories and mills in a town. The word was formerly used throughout Lancashire, but is now confined largely to the mill towns of Lancashire and Greater Manchester.

911 Mike Yarwood.

912 Winston Churchill.

913 Gracie Fields.

914 The Co-operative Movement.

915 The Wars of the Roses; Lancashire: red rose; Yorkshire: white rose.

916 250 miles; Edale, Derbyshire, to Kirk Yetholm in the Scottish Borders.

917 The South-West Peninsula Coast Path, 515 miles.

918 Cross Fell, Cumbria, 2930 feet.

919 60 inches in Upper Teesdale, Durham, and the Denbighshire Hills, Clwyd, in 1947.

920 Fish and chips.

921 The warp consists of the threads stretched lengthwise in the loom, to be crossed by the weft, the threads that run across the cloth.

922 Because weavers and cloth manufacturers came there to sell their lengths, or pieces, of cloth.

923 11,171,000; £24,985,000,000 (1986).

924 George Frederick Handel; in Dublin.

925 Women: soprano and alto; men: tenor and bass.

926 Rugby League.

927 Baritone, bombardon, cornet, euphonium, flugelhorn, saxhorn and trombone.

928 J.B. Priestley.

929 David Hockney.

930 *The Professor*, *Jane Eyre* and *Villette*; Anne and Emily.

931 Joseph Priestley, who was born at Birstall, now south of the motorway near Junction 27.

932 Leeds City; the club was reconstituted as Leeds United in 1920.

933 Four times: in 1965, 1970, 1972 and 1973; they won in 1972, when they defeated Arsenal 1–0.

934 92,986 (January to June 1986).

935 H.H. Asquith, who was born at Morley, near Junction 28.

936 4187.

937 Flour, salt, egg and milk.

938 As starters, with gravy, before the meat and vegetables are served.

939 The Aire and the Calder.

940 Henry Moore.

941 Rugby League.

942 Richard II.

943 Pomfret.

944 Liquorice.

945 Bewick's, Mute and Whooper.

946 About 20,000 miles, from the Arctic to the Antarctic and back.

947 110 square miles; 2,000 million tonnes.

948 *Mallard*; 126 mph.

949 Kings Cross; Waverley.

950 37,000 tons; 4000 MW.

951 Merry-go-rounds, so called because they make regular round trips between pits and power stations, loading and discharging on the move.

952 Bulk cargoes such as coal and coke, refuse, aggregates, grain, fertilizer etc.

953 1332 (1985).

954 The church of a monastery, or one to which a monastery was formerly attached.

955 The Ouse and the Trent.

956 4626 feet.

957 Spurn Head.

958 Philip Larkin.

959 Andrew Marvell.

960 William Wilberforce, who was born in Hull and became MP for the city in 1784.

961 Anthony Trollope.

M8

962 1.6 million (1985–86); 20.

963 Holyroodhouse.

964 The remains of an extinct volcano, 822 feet high, that dominates the Edinburgh skyline.

965 Alexander Graham Bell.

966 Princes Street.

967 The Castle and Holyroodhouse.

968 Pentland Hills.

969 James 'Paraffin' Young.

970 Sir James Simpson.

971 A series of election speeches made by W.E. Gladstone in southern Scotland and northern England in 1879 and 1880 condemning the foreign policy of the Tory government. The speeches, which helped to bring about a Liberal victory in the 1880 general election, were the first occasion on which a leading politician had wooed the electorate.

972 Twelve.

973 St Andrew.

974 The Act of Union, 1707.

975 About 80,000, mostly from the islands and the north-west of Scotland.

976 Two.

977 A street off Whitehall in London, formerly the headquarters of the Metropolitan Police (who now inhabit an office block known as New Scotland Yard in Victoria Street); Scotland Yard had previously been part of Whitehall Palace set aside for accommodation for the kings of Scotland.

978 Five: Lord Balfour (Prime Minister 1902–05); Sir Henry Campbell-Bannerman (1905–08); Andrew Bonar Law (1922–23); Ramsay MacDonald (1924, 1929–35); Sir Alec Douglas-Home (1963–64). In addition, Herbert Asquith (1908–16) represented a Scottish constituency, and Harold Macmillan (1957–63) was of

Scottish descent.

979   In 1975, when they lost 3–1 to Celtic.

980   106 miles; as the Daer Water in south Lanarkshire.

981   762,288 (1981).

982   Glasgow.

983   Celtic: green and white hooped shirts and white shorts. Rangers: royal blue shirts and white shorts.

984   At the end of the season in 1986, Rangers had won on 14 occasions, Celtic on 12.

985   1980; Celtic won 1–0.

986   Will Fyffe.

987   Amsterdam.

988   St Mungo.

989   Charles Rennie Mackintosh.

990   The Albert Memorial, the Foreign Office and the St Pancras Hotel.

991   Joseph Lister; much of his experimental work was done while he was Professor of Surgery at Glasgow University.

992   1896; 15.

993   London and Newcastle upon Tyne.

994   Copies woven in Paisley in silk or cotton of Eastern shawls sent home by Scottish officers in India.

995   The Prince of Wales.

996   1266 hours; May.

997   Hottest: 31.2°C on 4 August 1975; coldest: −17.4°C on 22 January 1940.

998   1971.

999   Mary Queen of Scots.

1000   It comes from the Gaelic *Dun Breatann*, which means Fort of the Britons; Dumbarton was capital of the kingdom of Strathclyde from the fifth to the early eleventh centuries.

M9

1001   Queen Margaret, wife of Malcolm III.

1002   51 miles; three: the Forth Road and Rail Bridges, and the Kincardine road bridge.

1003   Black; four.

1004   The Royal Scots Greys.

1005   He is Labour MP for Linlithgow.

1006   James I of Scotland.

1007   James V of Scotland and Mary Queen of Scots.

1008   Borrowstouness.

1009　The *Charlotte Dundas*, launched in 1802 on the Forth & Clyde Canal at Grangemouth, now north of the motorway at Junction 5.

1010　A turf wall built by the Roman Emperor Antoninus Pius between AD 137 and 161 from the Forth to the Clyde as a defence against the Caledonians. Rough Castle, west of Falkirk, is one of the best surviving parts of the wall.

1011　King Edward I of England, who in 1298 routed the Scottish forces under William Wallace.

1012　James Bruce, who came from Larbert, south of Junction 8.

1013　23 and 24 June 1314; Robert Bruce of Scotland and Edward II of England.

1014　The Bruce had about 5500 men, while the English army was 20,000 strong.

1015　Mary Queen of Scots and James VI.

1016　The Argyll and Sutherland Highlanders.

1017　The Universities of East Anglia, Essex, Kent, Lancaster, Sussex, Warwick and York.

1018　Flora Macdonald.

1019　The mountain peaks in Scotland over 3000 feet high.

1020　Ben Nevis, near Fort William; 4418 feet.

M90

1021　39,000 tons of steel; 405,000 cubic feet of concrete.

1022　Robert I, Robert Bruce.

1023　Andrew Carnegie.

1024　Malcolm Canmore; the remains of Malcolm Canmore's Tower can be seen in Pittencrief Park, Dunfermline.

1025　13 stations were opened, and none were closed.

1026　In 1785; the $ sign is a modification of the figure 8 that appeared on Spanish pieces of eight, the currency used in Britain's North American colonies at the time of their revolt.

1027　968,000 hectares, of which 92 per cent grows coniferous trees.

1028　John, Robert, James and William.

1029　Trout.

1030　Iceland, Greenland and Spitsbergen.

1031　A young page boy called Willy Douglas; he got hold of the keys of the castle, locked everyone into the Great Hall, and rowed Mary across the lake, dropping the keys in as he went (they were found 300 years later).

1032 Sir Alec Douglas-Home, who had just renounced his peerage in order to become Prime Minister.

1033 A fortified tower, with thick walls and battlemented parapets often protected by turrets at the corners. Burleigh Castle near Junction 7 is a typical example.

1034 Loch Lomond.

1035 Loughs.

1036 Stanley Adams.

1037 The Royal and Ancient; 1754.

1038 118 miles, the longest river in Scotland.

1039 Sir Walter Scott.

1040 Western Australia; the Swan.

1041 Charles II.